SCHOLASTIC
LITERATURE ANTHOLOGIES

POETRY

Edited by
Suzi Mee

CURRICULUM CONSULTANTS

Quality Quinn Sharp, M.A.
Language Arts Curriculum Specialist
San Marcos Unified School District
San Marcos, California

Helen Ruth Freeman
Director, New York City High School Poetry Contest
New York, New York

STAFF

Editorial Director:	Edward C. Haggerty
Poetry Unit Editor:	Marjorie L. Burns
Art Director:	Marijka Kostiw

Design of Scholastic Literature Anthologies based on concept by Joe Borzetta.

COVER ART: "Model With Unfinished Self-Portrait," by David Hockney. Oil on canvas. © David Hockney, 1977.

ISBN 0-590-35437-X

ACKNOWLEDGMENTS

Grateful acknowledgment is made to the following authors and publishers for the use of copyrighted materials. Every effort has been made to obtain permission to use previously published material. Any errors or omissions are unintentional.

Elizabeth Barnett, Literary Executor, for "Recuerdo" by Edna St. Vincent Millay. From COLLECTED POEMS, Harper & Row. Copyright 1922, 1950 by Edna St. Vincent Millay. Reprinted by permission.

Eric Berger for "The Ferry." Copyright © 1989 by Eric Berger.

Black Sparrow Press for "I Met a Genius" by Charles Bukowski. From BURNING IN WATER, DROWNING IN FLAME, © 1974. Reprinted by permission of the publisher.

Robert Bly for "Late Moon" from THIS TREE WILL BE HERE FOR A THOUSAND YEARS. Copyright © 1979 by Robert Bly. "Ode to My Socks" from NERUDA AND VALLEJO: SELECTED POEMS. Copyright © 1970 by Robert Bly. Reprinted by permission of Robert Bly.

Georges Borchardt, Inc. for "To Paint the Portrait of a Bird" and "Free Quarters" by Jacques Prevert. From PAROLES, published by Editions Gallimard, Paris. Reprinted by permission of Georges Borchardt, Inc. "The Instruction Manual" by John Ashbery. Reprinted by permission of Georges Borchardt, Inc. and the author. Copyright © 1956 by John Ashbery.

George Braziller, Inc. for "Fear" by Charles Simic. From DISMANTLING THE SILENCE. © 1971. Reprinted by permission of George Braziller, Inc.

Gwendolyn Brooks for "A Song in the Front Yard" from BLACKS, The David Company, copyright 1987. Reprinted by permission of the author.

Curtis Brown, Ltd. for "Miss Rosie," "Breaklight," and "The Thirty Eighth Year." Reprinted by permission of Curtis Brown, Ltd. Copyright © 1974 by Lucille Clifton.

The Witter Bynner Foundation for "A Green Stream" translated by Witter Bynner and first published in POETRY in 1922. Reprinted by permission of the Witter Bynner Foundation for Poetry, Inc., Santa Fe, New Mexico.

Doubleday & Company, Inc. for "Night Crow" by Theodore Roethke, copyright 1944 by Saturday Review Association, Inc. From THE COLLECTED POEMS OF THEODORE ROETHKE. "Child on Top of a Greenhouse" by Theodore Roethke. Copyright 1946 by Editorial Publications, Inc. From THE COLLECTED POEMS OF THEODORE ROETHKE. "Ancestors," "Celebration," "Dry and Parched," and "Kindergarten" from THE WHISPERING WIND by Terry Allen. Copyright © 1972 by the Institute of American Indian Arts. All reprinted by permission of Doubleday, a Division of Bantam, Doubleday, Dell Publishing Group, Inc.

Cornelius Eady for "Sarah Drives Me" and "My Childhood in Grease" from KARTUNES. Reprinted by permission of the author.

The Ecco Press for "Still Life" copyright © 1971, 1972, 1973, 1974, 1975 by Louise Gluck. From THE HOUSE ON MARSHLAND, first published by The Ecco Press in 1975. Reprinted by permission.

Editions Gallimard for "Free Quarters" and "To Paint the Portrait of a Bird" by Jacques Prevert from PAROLES, © Editions Gallimard 1949. Reprinted by permission of the publisher.

Faber and Faber Limited for "Digging." Reprinted by permission of Faber and Faber Ltd. from DEATH OF A NATURALIST by Seamus Heaney.

Farrar, Straus & Giroux, Inc. for "Digging," from POEMS 1965-1975 by Seamus Heaney. Copyright © 1966, 1969, 1972, 1980 by Seamus Heaney. Reprinted by permission of Farrar, Straus & Giroux, Inc. "Sam's World" by Sam Cornish from NATURAL PROCESS edited by Ted Wilenz and Tom Weatherly. Reprinted by permission of Hill and Wang, a division of Farrar, Straus & Giroux, Inc.

Edward Field for "Travel Song" from ESKIMO SONGS AND STORIES, translated by Edward Field. Published by Delacorte Press/Seymour Lawrence, 1973. Reprinted by permission of the author.

Acknowledgments continued on page 190.

CONTENTS

UNIT III: LOVE AND FRIENDSHIP

UNIT IV: SEEING AND FEELING

UNIT VII: MEMORIES AND DREAMS

INTRODUCTION

The poet W.H. Auden aptly described poetry as "a language within a language." He meant that, within the language we use for discussing and managing the surface things of life, there is another language that reaches below the surface. This second language, poetry, awakens us to new possibilities of perception and feeling. Once we are made aware of these possibilities, our lives become so much richer that we are no longer satisfied with mere surfaces.

Poetry also dusts off the five senses of seeing, hearing, touching, smelling, and tasting, thereby making us more alert and more responsive to our surroundings.

In addition, poetry helps us to remember our past, and, by remembering, to understand that the things that make us different and the things that make us alike are of equal importance.

But perhaps the most singular gift of poetry is that it can transform, by the power of the imagination, something ordinary into something extraordinary. In this sense, poetry is truly miraculous.

The poems in this anthology were chosen to demonstrate the qualities of poetry in a variety of ways. They are amusing, sad, wistful, joyful, poignant; they are about experiences that young people can recognize and identify with.

We hope they give pleasure.

SELF-PORTRAITS

• An "autobiographia literaria" (literary autobiography) is an author's own story of his or her life as a writer. The author of this poem, Frank O'Hara, seems both delighted and surprised that he grew up to be a poet.

Frank O'Hara

AUTOBIOGRAPHIA LITERARIA

When I was a child
I played by myself in a
corner of the schoolyard
all alone.

I hated dolls and I
hated games, animals were
not friendly and birds
flew away.

If anyone was looking
for me I hid behind a
tree and cried out "I am
an orphan."

And here I am, the
center of all beauty!
writing these poems!
Imagine!

A CLOSER LOOK

1. Judging from the first three stanzas of the poem, how was Frank O'Hara different from most other children?

2. What does the poet mean when he says that he is "the center of all beauty"?

3. Do you think it is surprising that the child described in this poem grew up to be a poet? Explain your answer.

● Have you ever put off a task until tomorrow, and then, when tomorrow came, put it off again until the next day . . . and the next day . . . and the next? If you have ever procrastinated in this way, you'll understand the feelings of the speaker in this poem.

W.S. Merwin

SOMETHING I'VE NOT DONE

Something I've not done
is following me
I haven't done it again and again
so it has many footsteps
like a drumstick that's grown old and never been used

In late afternoon I hear it come closer
at times it climbs out of a sea
onto my shoulders
and I shrug it off
losing one more chance

Every morning
it's drunk up part of my breath for the day
and knows which way
I'm going
and already it's not done there

But once more I say I'll lay hands on it
tomorrow
and add its footsteps to my heart
and its story to my regrets
and its silence to my compass

A CLOSER LOOK

1. What do you think the "something" might be?

2. Does the speaker feel guilty about not doing the "something"? Find lines in the poem that support your answer.

3. If the speaker finally takes care of the "something," what will happen?

● Conceited people tend to be pretty well satisfied with themselves. When they examine their own appearance or character, they don't see any important flaws. They don't even see much room for improvement! What is the speaker in this poem conceited about?

Elizabeth Ruiz

CONCEIT

I looked in the mirror.
Handsome is as handsome does, I thought.
So I decided to do something handsome
Because actions speak louder than words.
After acting handsome,
I looked in the mirror again.
Beauty is only skin deep. I thought,
I must have thick skin.

A CLOSER LOOK

1. Elizabeth Ruiz made a fresh, original poem out of four clichés by cleverly arranging them in a certain order. (A cliché is a trite, overused expression; for example, "Money talks" and "Birds of a feather flock together" are clichés. These ready-made phrases enable us to talk without thinking, and that's probably why we use them so much.) What are the four clichés in the poem? Which cliché shows most clearly that the speaker is conceited?

2. What handsome act do you think the speaker might have performed?

3. One idea that you might get from this poem is that only a shallow thinker — someone who thought in clichés — could be conceited. Do you agree or disagree with this idea? Explain your answer.

• The poet remembers warm summer nights in her girlhood, when she liked to lie outside on the grass and gaze up at the stars. Then it seemed to her young mind that the stars looked down wisely, as if they knew the answers to her questions.

Anne Sexton

YOUNG

A thousand doors ago
when I was a lonely kid
in a big house with four
garages and it was summer
as long as I could remember,
I lay on the lawn at night,
clover wrinkling under me,
the wise stars bedding over me,
my mother's window, half shut,
an eye where sleepers pass,
and the boards of the house
were smooth and white as wax
and probably a million leaves
wailed on their strange stalks
as the crickets ticked together
and I, in my brand new body,
which was not a woman's yet,
told the stars my questions
and thought God could really see
the heat and the painted light,
elbows, knees, dreams, goodnight.

A CLOSER LOOK

1. The poet says that the events of the poem took place "a thousand doors ago." She means that time has passed, of course; but she also means something else. What happens when a person goes through a door? What might going through a door symbolize (stand for)?

2. Find two details in the poem that appeal to the sense of sight. Find two details that appeal to the sense of hearing.

● There is disappointment in Lucille Clifton's voice as she describes herself as just "an ordinary woman." She had hoped to be wiser, more "afrikan," more like her extraordinary mother, who died early.

Lucille Clifton

THE THIRTY EIGHTH YEAR

the thirty eighth year
of my life,
plain as bread
round as a cake
an ordinary woman.

an ordinary woman.

i had expected to be
smaller than this,
more beautiful,
wiser in afrikan ways,
more confident,
i had expected
more than this.

i will be forty soon.
my mother once was forty.

my mother died at forty four,
a woman of sad countenance
leaving behind a girl
awkward as a stork.
my mother was thick,
her hair was a jungle and
she was very wise
and beautiful
and sad.

i have dreamed dreams
for you mama
more than once.
i have wrapped me

in your skin
and made you live again
more than once.
i have taken the bones you hardened
and built daughters
and they blossom and promise fruit
like afrikan trees.
i am a woman now.
an ordinary woman.

in the thirty eighth
year of my life,
surrounded by life,
a perfect picture of
blackness blessed,
i had not expected this
loneliness.

if it is western,
if it is the final
europe in my mind,
if in the middle of my life
i am turning the final turn
into the shining dark
let me come to it whole
and holy
not afraid
not lonely
out of my mother's life
into my own.
into my own.

i had expected more than this.
i had not expected to be
an ordinary woman.

A CLOSER LOOK

1. What has the poet done to make her mother "live again"?

2. Considering that Lucille Clifton wrote this poem, do you agree that she is an "ordinary woman"? Why or why not?

● Life's shocks and misfortunes seem easier to bear if you have a special place where you can go to sit alone and think. Such a place is described in "The Room That's In Between."

Angela Lee

THE ROOM THAT'S IN BETWEEN

When I want to be alone,
I go right over to a small room
between the kitchen and the living room.

In the room are small knick-knacks,
a folding bed, chairs, cloth
and some shelves.

When I'm in the room,
I close the door.
The closed door gives me a sense of secrecy.

I sit on the folding bed
and look around: the bags are messed up again
but the place is quiet.

The shape of the room is strange:
like a square
with the corner lopped off.

A window faces the alley
where cats sit around
licking themselves clean.

The white walls of the room
are gradually getting dirty.
I stay here until I feel better,

then I go back to my own room.

A CLOSER LOOK

1. Do you think the speaker's family uses the room that's in between on a daily basis? If not, how is the room used? Give details from the poem that support your answer.

2. What reasons might the speaker have for going to the small in-between room when she is upset, rather than to her own room?

● We feel close to animals because we are animals too. But how much do we have in common with plants? Can there be any kinship between a tree, for instance, and a person? Robert Frost says yes.

Robert Frost

TREE AT MY WINDOW

Tree at my window, window tree,
My sash is lowered when night comes on;
But let there never be curtain drawn
Between you and me.

Vague dream-head lifted out of the ground,
And thing next most diffuse to cloud,
Not all your light tongues talking aloud
Could be profound.

But tree, I have seen you taken and tossed,
And if you have seen me when I slept,
You have seen me when I was taken and swept
And all but lost.

That day she put our heads together,
Fate had her imagination about her,
Your head so much concerned with outer,
Mine with inner, weather.

A CLOSER LOOK

1. According to Frost, does the tree's head look much like a human head? (The head of a tree is the part that has leaves.) To answer this question, find the phrase that Frost uses to describe the tree's head.

2. What are the tree's "light tongues"? What can human tongues do that the tree's "tongues" cannot?

3. Frost says that he and the tree have one important thing in common: both their heads are buffeted by weather. What is the "outer weather" that affects the tree? What is the "inner weather" that affects the poet?

● Has this ever happened to you: You are looking at some common, everyday object, and suddenly you are struck with a strange memory. That object — the same and yet different, more mysterious — has appeared to you before, in a dream. "Night Crow" is about that kind of experience.

Theodore Roethke

NIGHT CROW

When I saw that clumsy crow
Flap from a wasted tree,
A shape in the mind rose up:
Over the gulfs of dream
Flew a tremendous bird
Further and further away
Into a moonless black,
Deep in the brain, far back.

A CLOSER LOOK

1. The poet mentions two birds. Which of the two exists in the real world, and which exists only in the poet's mind?

2. Which of the two birds is more interesting or important to the poet? If you're not sure, look again at the title of the poem. The title tells you which bird the poet is really writing about.

3. The clumsy crow that flaps from a dead tree reminds the poet of something he has seen in a dream. Do you think the dream was a pleasant one? If not, what adjective(s) would you use to describe the dream?

● As a boy, Wordsworth spent many happy hours roaming the hills and valleys of the Lake District in England. In these lines he tells how he would stand by the lake at evening and imitate the hooting of the owls so well that they would hoot back at him!

William Wordsworth

LINES FROM "THE PRELUDE"

There was a Boy: ye knew him well, ye cliffs
And islands of Winander! — many a time
At evening, when the earliest stars began
To move along the edges of the hills,
Rising or setting, would he stand alone
Beneath the trees or by the glimmering lake,
And there, with fingers interwoven, both hands
Pressed closely palm to palm, and to his mouth
Uplifted, he, as through an instrument,
Blew mimic hootings to the silent owls,
That they might answer him; and they would shout
Across the watery vale, and shout again,
Responsive to his call, with quivering peals,
And long halloos and screams, and echoes loud,
Redoubled and redoubled, concourse wild
Of jocund din; and, when a lengthened pause
Of silence came and baffled his best skill,
Then sometimes, in that silence while he hung
Listening, a gentle shock of mild surprise
Has carried far into his heart the voice
Of mountain torrents; or the visible scene
Would enter unawares into his mind,
With all its solemn imagery, its rocks,
Its woods, and that uncertain heaven, received
Into the bosom of the steady lake.

A CLOSER LOOK

1. Sometimes the owls would break off their conversation with the Boy. What did the Boy sometimes hear in the silence?

2. Do you think that the sounds and sights of nature made a lasting impression on the Boy? Explain your answer.

• Early childhood is a special state of mind, one that most people forget soon after they grow out of it. This poem will help you either remember or imagine the strange fantasy world that exists inside the head of a small child.

Donald Hall

THE CHILD

He lives among a dog,
a tricycle, and a friend.
Nobody owns him.

He walks by himself, beside
the black pool, in the cave
where icicles of rock
rain hard water,
and the walls are rough
with the light of stone.

He hears low talking
without words.
The hand of a wind touches him.

He walks until he is tired
or somebody calls him.
He leaves right away.

When he plays with his friend
he stops suddenly
to hear the black water.

A CLOSER LOOK

1. Why does "nobody own" the child?

2. Name some of the things that the child sees and hears in the private world inside his mind.

3. The child's mind and personality are still unformed, but basic tendencies are already present within him. What image in the poem might represent these tendencies? Explain your choice.

● The speaker in this poem is a young girl who thinks her mother is too strict. The girl is tired of being told that she can't do this, and she shouldn't do that, and she mustn't stray out of the safe (and boring!) front yard.

Gwendolyn Brooks

A SONG IN THE FRONT YARD

I've stayed in the front yard all my life.
I want a peek at the back
Where it's rough and untended and hungry weed grows.
A girl gets sick of a rose.

I want to go in the back yard now
And maybe down the alley,
To where the charity children play.
I want a good time today.

They do some wonderful things.
They have some wonderful fun.
My mother sneers, but I say it's fine
How they don't have to go in at quarter to nine.

My mother, she tells me that Johnnie Mae
Will grow up to be a bad woman.
That George'll be taken to Jail soon or late
(On account of last winter he sold our back gate).

But I say it's fine. Honest, I do.
And I'd like to be a bad woman, too,
And wear the brave stockings of night-black lace
And strut down the streets with paint on my face.

A CLOSER LOOK

1. *The front yard represents safe and proper behavior. What do you think the back yard and the alley represent?*

2. *What do you think makes children wish to imitate people who break the rules of polite society? Why do such people often seem glamorous to children?*

● In this poem, Sylvia Plath imagines a mirror that does more than just reflect the objects before it. It actually sees and thinks, and even talks about its observations and itself.

Sylvia Plath

MIRROR

I am silver and exact.
Whatever I see I swallow immediately
Just as it is, unmisted by love or dislike.
I am not cruel, only truthful —
The eye of a little god, four-cornered.
Most of the time I meditate on the opposite wall.
It is pink, with speckles. I have looked at it so long
I think it is a part of my heart. But it flickers.
Faces and darkness separate us over and over.

Now I am a lake. A woman bends over me,
Searching my reaches for what she really is.
Then she turns to those liars, the candles or the moon.
I see her back, and reflect it faithfully.
She rewards me with tears and an agitation of hands.
I am important to her. She comes and goes.
Each morning it is her face that replaces the darkness.
In me she has drowned a young girl, and in me an old woman
Rises toward her day after day, like a terrible fish.

A CLOSER LOOK

1. In what sense does the mirror "swallow" whatever it sees?

2. The second stanza starts with a metaphor: "Now I am a lake." (A metaphor is an implied comparison. It says that two things are similar without using the word "like." This metaphor says that the mirror is [like] a lake.) In what way(s) is a mirror like a lake?

3. Why is the mirror important to the woman?

• Walt Whitman believed that people are deeply affected and even changed by the commonplace sights and sounds of everyday life. Do you think he was right? Or do you think his idea applies only to people like Whitman himself — people who are open to the world around them and full of the joy of living?

Walt Whitman

THERE WAS A CHILD WENT FORTH

There was a child went forth every day,
And the first object he looked upon and received with wonder or
    pity or love or dread, that object he became,
And that object became part of him for the day or a certain part
    of the day . . . or for many years or stretching cycles of
    years.
The early lilacs became part of this child,
And grass, and white and red morningglories, and white and red
    clover, and the song of the phoebe-bird,
And the March-born lambs, and the sow's pink-faint litter,
    and the mare's foal, and the cow's calf, and the noisy
    brood of the
barnyard . . . all became a part of him.

And the field-sprout of April and May became part of him . . .
And the appletrees covered with blossoms and the fruit afterward
    And the schoolmistress that passed on her way to the
    school . . .
And all the changes of city and country wherever he went.

The mother at home quietly placing the dishes on the supper-
    table,
The mother with mild words . . .

The father, strong, self-sufficient, manly, mean, angered,
    unjust, . . .
The family usages, the language, the company, the furniture . . .
    the yearning and swelling heart, . . .
The doubts of daytime and the doubts of nighttime . . .
Whether that which appears so is so . . .
Men and women crowding fast in the streets . . .
The streets themselves, and the façades of houses . . .
The village on the highland seen from afar at sunset . . .
The schooner nearby sleepily dropping down the tide . . .
The hurrying tumbling waves and quickbroken crests and
    slapping;
The strata of colored clouds . . .
The horizon's edge, the flying seacrow, the fragrance of saltmarsh
    and shoremud;
These became part of that child who went forth every day, and
    who now goes and will always go forth every day,
And these become part of him or her that peruses them now.

A CLOSER LOOK

1. *What are some of the emotions the child felt as he observed the world around him?*

2. *What do you think happened when the child saw an object to which he did not react emotionally? Did that object become part of him? Find evidence in the poem to support your answer.*

3. *In the last line, Whitman refers to "him or her" who now peruses (considers, thinks about) the sights, smells, sounds, and feelings he has listed. He means you, the reader! What effect does Whitman think your reading of his poem will have on you?*

FAMILY PORTRAITS

● A memory is like a movie, except that you don't just play it back. You "film" the memory as you watch it move across the screen of your mind. You can shoot the scene from a middle distance, then zoom in to focus on a detail, than back off to get a wider perspective. Can you follow the movements of the camera in the poem below?

Roy Scheele

A KITCHEN MEMORY

My mother is peeling an apple over the sink,
her two deft hands effortless and intent.
The skin comes away in the shape of a corkscrew,
red and white by turns, with a shimmer of rose
where the blade in its turn cuts close: a blush,
called out of hiding like a second skin.
Now the apple fattens in her hand;
the last scrap of parings falls away;
and she halves and sections the white grainy meat,
picks up another apple, brushes back
the dark hair at her temple with the knife hand.
The only sound is the fan stirring the heat.

A CLOSER LOOK

1. What reason might the poet have had for recording such an ordinary event?

2. List some of the sensory details that the poet uses to make the "moving picture" vivid. To what senses do the details appeal?

• The poet looks back at a scene from his youth that he and his father acted out many times. And in that scene he now sees a truth about his father that he didn't understand then.

Robert Hayden

THOSE WINTER SUNDAYS

Sundays too my father got up early
and put his clothes on in the blueblack cold,
then with cracked hands that ached
from labor in the weekday weather made
banked fires blaze. No one ever thanked him.

I'd wake and hear the cold splintering, breaking.
When the rooms were warm, he'd call,
and slowly I would rise and dress,
fearing the chronic angers of that house,

Speaking indifferently to him,
who had driven out the cold
and polished my good shoes as well.
What did I know, what did I know
of love's austere and lonely offices?

A CLOSER LOOK

1. What do you learn in the first stanza about the father's daily life and work?

2. Choose one of these phrases and tell what you think it means in the poem: "blueblack cold"; "cold splintering, breaking"; "the chronic angers of that house."

3. What does the poem tell you about the boy's relationship with his father? What does the speaker understand now about his father that he didn't understand as a boy?

● We all have our own ideas about what is important in life and what is not worth fussing about. If we act according to our beliefs, we can, to some extent, make our own world.

Sam Cornish

SAM'S WORLD

sam's mother has
grey combed hair

she will not touch
it with a hot iron

she leaves it
the way the lord
intended

she wears it proudly
a black and grey
round head of hair

A CLOSER LOOK

1. What do you think Sam's mother would say if someone told her that her hair would look nicer if she curled it with a curling iron?

2. Sam's mother takes pride in the plainness of her hair style. Given this fact, what can you guess about her clothing, the furnishings of her house, and other aspects of her lifestyle?

3. Why is the poem called "Sam's World"?

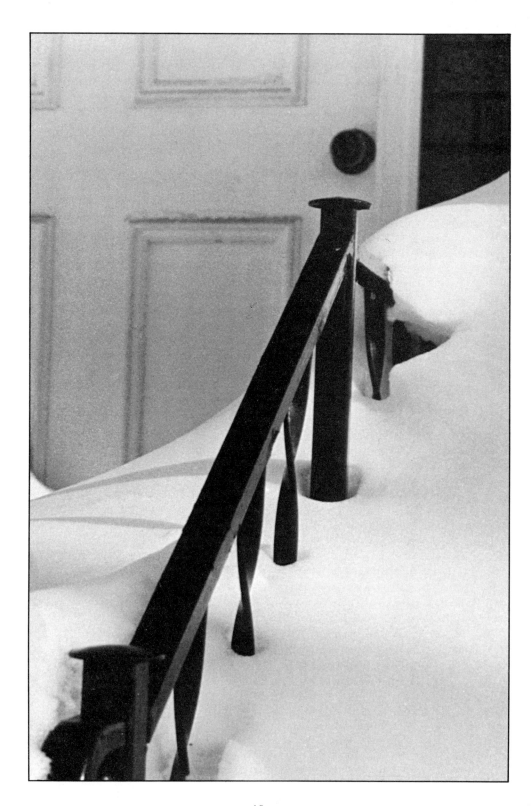

• Occasionally you share with another person an experience in which some object plays an important part. After that, there may always be a meaningful connection in your mind between that person and that object.

John Noyer

MY FATHER AND MY SLED

It was very cold,
   snow covered the ground.
My father was coming, I was told.
   I had not seen him for some time.
He was so tall
   and his eyes were large and blue.
I was small
   but I also had blue eyes.
We took my sled
   out into the cold
and that great big man
   ran before and pulled me
along.

A CLOSER LOOK

1. What do the third and fourth lines of the poem tell you about the boy's family?

2. What action performed by the father shows that he wants to make the boy happy?

3. What object mentioned in the poem gives the father a chance to show his love for his son?

● The coat described in this poem is not made of cloth. It is an imaginary coat made from the poet's memories of objects, places, and feelings that she associates with her father.

Suzi Mee

MY FATHER'S COAT

My father's coat was made
of finest muscle. Fish-scales
were its lining;
from them, water-falls
glistened. Rainbow trout
swam in the depths of its pockets
among twigs and polished stones.
Inside this coat, my father
was invisible. He became
the smell of wet leaves,
the smoke of campfires,
and when he wrapped me in his
sleeves, I stepped inside
the dark forest.

A CLOSER LOOK

1. The poem gives you clues to some of the activities that the father enjoyed. Name at least two.

2. Suggest a reason why the poet's memories of her father are linked with the memory of his coat.

● Have you ever met a person who had a great idea for saving the world, or at least for improving it? If you have met such a person, did he or she try to sell you on the idea? Did you buy it? The speaker in this poem seems to have sold one family on the benefits of expressing their affection more openly. He tells someone named Harry what happened.

Robert Hershon

OPENLY EXPRESSED AFFECTION BETWEEN MEMBERS OF THE FAMILY UNIT

then i call the children
back into the dining room

you're a very lucky little girl you know that
why don't you give your father a great big kiss
for what he's done for you today and don't forget
your mother and say honey have you got one for me too
and you son are you too old to kiss your father
sure go ahead go ahead and your mother
what's wrong with your mother sure go ahead
and missus why not give your husband a kiss too
sure he's a good fella sure
go on dad kiss them all you can be proud
of what you've done for them today
go on sis give your brother a kiss
go ahead boy kiss her again sure
and they're all chasing each other
around that table kissing each other
and hugging each other and kissing each other
and kissing each other sure kissing each other

believe me harry that's one sale
that'll never cancel

A CLOSER LOOK

1. *Who do you think the speaker of the poem might be? Do you think he's a member of the family? a close friend? a dinner guest?*

2. *What is the sale that the speaker refers to in the last two lines? Do you think he is right in assuming that the sale will never be cancelled?*

3. *Does more hugging and kissing necessarily mean more genuine affection? Give reasons for your answer.*

● The poet compares his work tool, a pen, with the spades wielded by his Irish father and grandfather. He remembers how skillful his father was at digging potatoes and how fast and neatly his grandfather cut turf on Toner's bog. (Turf is the upper layer of soil that's matted with grass. A bog is an area of wet, spongy ground.)

Seamus Heaney

DIGGING

Between my finger and my thumb
The squat pen rests: snug as a gun.

Under my window, a clean rasping sound
When the spade sinks into gravelly ground:
My father, digging. I look down

Till his straining rump among the flowerbeds
Bends low, comes up twenty years away
Stooping in rhythm through potato drills
Where he was digging.

The coarse boot nestled on the lug, the shaft
Against the inside knee was levered firmly.
He rooted out tall tops, buried the bright edge deep
To scatter new potatoes that we picked
Loving their cool hardness in our hands.

By God, the old man could handle a spade.
Just like his old man.

My grandfather cut more turf in a day
Than any other man on Toner's bog.
Once I carried him milk, in a bottle
Corked sloppily with paper. He straightened up
To drink it, then fell to right away

Nicking and slicing neatly, heaving sods
Over his shoulder, going down and down
For the good turf. Digging.

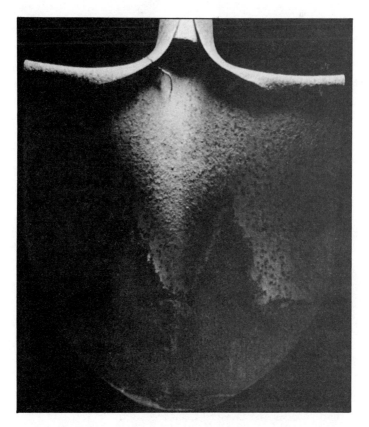

The cold smell of potato mould, the squelch and slap
Of soggy peat, the curt cuts of an edge
Through living roots awaken in my head.
But I've no spade to follow men like them.

Between my finger and my thumb
The squat pen rests.
I'll dig with it.

A CLOSER LOOK

1. Where is the poet at the beginning of the poem? Where is his father? What starts the poet thinking about the past?

2. Does the poet feel that his father and grandfather were inferior to him because they did manual labor? Or does he respect and admire them? Find evidence in the poem to support your answer.

3. What does the poet mean when he says he will "dig" with his pen?

● One of the most treasured of all human images is that of the loving mother watching over her child while he sleeps.

Robert Francis

WHILE I SLEPT

While I slept, while I slept and the night grew colder
She would come to my bedroom stepping softly
And draw a blanket about my shoulder
While I slept.

While I slept, while I slept in the dark still heat
She would come to my bedside stepping coolly
And smooth the twisted troubled sheet
While I slept.

Now she sleeps, sleeps under quiet rain
While nights grow warm or nights grow colder
And I wake and sleep and wake again
While she sleeps.

A CLOSER LOOK

1. How did the mother care for the boy on winter nights? How did she care for him on summer nights?

2. What is the meaning of the line "Now she sleeps, sleeps under quiet rain"?

● What happens when you look at a family portrait that includes you? Usually you play the role of a spectator, viewing the picture from the outside. But sometimes you may mentally put yourself back inside the picture and, facing the camera, see what you saw then.

Louise Gluck

STILL LIFE

Father has his arm around Tereze.
She squints. My thumb
is in my mouth: my fifth autumn.
Near the copper beech
the spaniel dozes in shadows.
Not one of us does not avert his eyes.

Across the lawn, in full sun, my mother
stands behind her camera.

A CLOSER LOOK

1. The poem describes a scene from the past. Which part of the scene shows in the photograph? Which part of the scene is outside the photograph?

2. Why is Tereze squinting? Why are all the people in the photo looking off to one side instead of straight at the camera?

3. Is "Still Life" an appropriate name for this poem? Why or why not?

• The speaker's ancestors were members of one of the Plains Indian tribes. They lived in harmony with the land, and now they are part of the land. What else, besides the dust of their bodies, is left of the ancestors and their way of life?

Grey Cohoe

ANCESTORS

On the wind-beaten plains
    once lived my ancestors.
In the days of peaceful moods,
    they wandered and hunted.
In days of need or greed,
    they warred and loafed.
Beneath the lazy sun, kind winds above,
    they laughed and feasted.
Through the starlit night, under the moon,
    they dreamed and loved.
Now, from the wind-beaten plains,
    only their dust rises.

A CLOSER LOOK

1. Are the present-day members of the speaker's tribe carrying on the traditions of the ancestors? Find evidence in the poem to support your answer.

2. What emotion do you think the speaker feels when he thinks about the ancestors?

● We often assume that old people are full of wisdom and knowledge just because they have lived for many years. We also assume that they have a duty to share their wisdom with anyone who asks. But the old men in this poem refuse to speak. They won't even give directions to a lost traveler. Could it be that they don't have any answers?

Donald Justice

THE GRANDFATHERS

Why will they never sleep?
                John Peale Bishop

Why will they never speak,
The old ones, the grandfathers?
Always you find them sitting
On ruined porches, deep
In the back country, at dusk,
Hawking and spitting.
They might have been there forever,
Tapping their sticks,
Peevish, discredited gods.
Ask of the traveler how,
At road end, they will fix
You maybe with the cold
Eye of a snake or a bird
And answer not a word,
Only these blank, oracular
Headshakes or headnods.

A CLOSER LOOK

1. The word "discredited" means "no longer believed." How do you think this word might apply to the old men in the poem?

2. The word "oracular" means "vague and ambiguous, open to more than one interpretation." What oracular gestures do the old men make when the traveler asks them questions? Why are these gestures unhelpful?

3. Why do the old men refuse to speak? (Give your opinion.)

● In most cultures, including our own, it is customary to pay close, respectful attention to the last words of a dying person. Sometimes the words give listeners an insight into the person's life or even into life — and death — in general.

William Carlos Williams

THE LAST WORDS OF MY ENGLISH GRANDMOTHER

There were some dirty plates
and a glass of milk
beside her on a small table
near the rank, disheveled bed —

Wrinkled and nearly blind
she lay and snored
rousing with anger in her tones
to cry for food,

Gimme something to eat —
They're starving me —
I'm all right I won't go
to the hospital. No, no, no

Give me something to eat
Let me take you
to the hospital, I said
and after you are well

you can do as you please.
She smiled, Yes
you do what you please first
then I can do what I please —

Oh, oh, oh! she cried
as the ambulance men lifted
her in the stretcher —
Is this what you call

making me comfortable?
By now her mind was clear —
Oh you think you're smart
you young people,

she said, but I'll tell you
you don't know anything
Then we started.
On the way

we passed a long row
of elms. She looked at them
awhile out of
the ambulance window and said,

What are all those
fuzzy-looking things out there?
Trees? Well I'm tired
of them and rolled her head away.

A CLOSER LOOK

1. We can infer that William Carlos Williams, who was a medical doctor, attended his grandmother in her last illness. In the poem, how does the grandmother feel about the treatment she is receiving? What does she think of the doctor's decision to take her to the hospital?

2. Find lines in the poem in which the grandmother lets her grandson know that she is not impressed by his knowledge. Find lines in which she shows that she is not fooled by the bargain he is offering her: "Give me control now and I'll give it back to you later, when you're well."

3. The words "I'm tired of them" might mean "I'm tired of them and tired of living." Or the words might mean "So what does it matter if I couldn't tell they were trees? I don't care about them anyway." Which of these two meanings do you think is more likely?

● Here is a whole poem built on a single simile. As you know, a simile surprises by pointing out a likeness between two things that appear unlike. Usually the two things turn out to be similar in only one or two ways. But Christine Bader lists no fewer than six similarities between her sister and a balloon. And shape isn't one of them!

Christine Bader

MY SISTER IS LIKE A BALLOON

My sister is like a balloon because she has her own ideas but is tied down by a parental string.

My sister is like a balloon because she wants to be free and floating — and sometimes is.

My sister is like a balloon because when her idea is punctured, she becomes lifeless.

My sister is like a balloon because she never seems to run out of pep or energy.

My sister is like a balloon because she has many peers, though none exactly like her.

My sister is like a balloon because she acts as though she's above . . . everybody.

A CLOSER LOOK

1. What does the speaker seem to admire in her sister?

2. Is there anything about her sister that the speaker does not admire? If so, what is it?

● The poet pays tribute to a hurt and orphaned kitten and to the one member of her family who knew what to do about it.

Nikki Giovanni

A POEM FOR CAROL

(May she always wear red ribbons)

when i was very little
though it's still true today
there were no sidewalks in lincoln heights
and the home we had on jackson street
was right next to a bus stop and a sewer
which didn't really ever become offensive
but one day from the sewer a little kitten
with one eye gone
came crawling out
though she never really came into our yard but just
sort of hung by to watch the folk
my sister who was always softhearted but able
to act effectively started taking milk
out to her while our father would only say
don't bring *him* home and everyday
after school i would rush home to see if she was still
there and if gary had fed her but i could never
bring myself to go near her
she was so loving
and so hurt and so singularly beautiful and i knew
i had nothing to give that would
replace her one gone eye
and if i had named her which i didn't i'm sure
i would have called her carol

A CLOSER LOOK

1. Why is it sometimes difficult for a softhearted person to act effectively?

2. Why couldn't the poet bring herself to go near the kitten?

3. What makes a person like certain names better than others? By what standard does a person judge one name to be more appropriate than another? (These questions ask for your opinion; there are no right or wrong answers.)

● The poet Gary Snyder takes nature as his subject. In this poem, he writes about two of nature's many families. The first one is his own: himself, his wife Masa, and their sons. The second family is non-human, but it, too, has its place in nature.

Gary Snyder

ALL IN THE FAMILY

For the first time in memory
heavy rain in August
   tuning up the chainsaw
     begin to cut oak
Boletus by the dozen
   fruiting in the woods
Full moon, warm nights
   the boys learn to float
Masa gone off dancing
   for another thirty days
Queen Anne's Lace in the meadow
   a Flicker's single call

Oregano, lavender, the *salvia* sage
   wild pennyroyal
   from the Yuba River bank
All in the family
   of Mint.

A CLOSER LOOK

1. Where do you think the poet's family probably lives?

2. Where would you be likely to see more different types of families: in the city or in the country?

3. Do you think it is possible to learn about the human family by observing non-human families? Why or why not?

● The poet declares that summer is the best of all seasons in her hometown and lists many convincing reasons why.

Nikki Giovanni

KNOXVILLE, TENNESSEE

I always like summer
best
you can eat fresh corn
from daddy's garden
and okra
and greens
and cabbage
and lots of
barbecue
and buttermilk
and homemade ice-cream
at the church picnic
and listen to
gospel music
outside
at the church
homecoming
and go to the mountains with
your grandfather
and go barefooted
and be warm
all the time
not only when you go to bed
and sleep.

A CLOSER LOOK

1. The poet is writing about the past, but the speaker in the poem uses the present tense. Who is the speaker? Do you think this use of the present tense makes the poem more effective? Why or why not?

2. Reread the list of sensory pleasures that the speaker enjoys in the summer. What three senses are involved in these pleasures?

UNIT III

LOVE AND FRIENDSHIP

● Every reader who knows what remorse feels like will understand this poem. Every reader who has ever thought, "How could I have done such a terrible thing?" will understand this poem. Every reader who has ever thought, "If only I could go back and live that day again!" will understand this poem. In other words, every reader will understand this poem.

David Huddle

ICICLE

I smacked you in the mouth for no good reason
except that the icicle had broken off
so easily and that it felt like a club
in my hand, and so I swung it, the soft
part of your lower lip sprouting a drop,
then gushing a trail onto the snow even
though we both squeezed the place with our fingers.
I'd give a lot not to be the swinger
of that icicle. I'd like another
morning just like that, cold, windy, and bright
as Russia, your glasses fogging up, your face
turning to me again. I tell you I might
help both our lives by changing that act to this,
by handing you the ice, a gift, my brother.

A CLOSER LOOK

1. How much time passed before the speaker began to regret what he had done? How did he show his regret?

2. Did the speaker's hurtful act have any lasting effect on his brother's life or his own? Find evidence in the poem to support your answer.

3. "What's done cannot be undone," says Lady Macbeth in Shakespeare's play. True, but if the misdeed is less serious than Lady Macbeth's was (hers was murder), can a kind deed make up for it? For example, do you think this poem might help heal the wounds that both brothers suffered? Give reasons for your answer.

• When you and your best friend get together, where do you like to go and what do you like to do? Judging from what he says in this poem, the speaker and his friend like to go someplace and eat!

Cornelius Eady

SARAH DRIVES ME
(to the gates of fatness)

I have dreams of you
sitting me down before pillars of food,
driving me to
the gates
of fatness.
this poem
shouldn't be read
it should be eaten,
dear friend,
it should be eaten.

I have dreams of us
walking down
the street
together.
we fill up
the sidewalk.
people walk
the other way
when they see us
coming.

A CLOSER LOOK

1. Suppose you were going to draw a picture to illustrate this poem. What would the "gates of fatness" look like in your picture? What else would your drawing show?

2. What is the tone of this poem? To answer this question, think about the poet's attitude toward his subject. Does he seem to be disturbed, worried, or angry? Or does he seem to be amused by the situation?

● This poem by Sharon Olds is dedicated and addressed to a childhood friend who died before reaching her tenth birthday. Two images in the poem — hair and a brick path — are used to connect the past and the present.

Sharon Olds

BEST FRIENDS

(for Elizabeth Ewer, 1942-51)

The day my daughter turned ten, I thought of the
lank, glittering, greenish cap of your
gold hair. The last week of
your life, when I came each day after school,
I'd study the path to your front door,
the bricks laid close as your hairs. I'd try to
read the pattern, frowning down
for a sign.
           The last day — there was not
a mark on that walk, not a stone out of place —
the nurses would not let me in.

We were nine. We had never mentioned death
or growing up. I had no more imagined
you dead
than you imagined me
a mother. But when I had a daughter
I named her for you, as if pulling you back
through a crack between the bricks.
             She is ten now, Liddy.
She has outlived you, her dark hair gleaming like
the earth into which the path was pressed,
the path to you.

66

A CLOSER LOOK

1. Why did her daughter's tenth birthday make the poet think of her childhood friend?

2. Why did the poet name her daughter Elizabeth? To what does she compare the color of her daughter's hair?

3. What path led the poet to her friend when the friend was alive? Is there any "path" to her friend now? If so, what is it?

- On seeing an impoverished elderly black woman, the poet resolves anew that her own and later generations shall have a better life.

Lucille Clifton

MISS ROSIE

when i watch you
wrapped up like garbage
sitting, surrounded by the smell
of too old potato peels
or
when i watch you
in your old man's shoes
with the little toe cut out
sitting, waiting for your mind
like next week's grocery
I say
when I watch you
you wet brown bag of a woman
who used to be the best looking gal in georgia
used to be called the Georgia Rose
i stand up
through your destruction
i stand up

A CLOSER LOOK

1. Using the clues the poet gives you, describe the setting and the main character, Miss Rosie.

2. What does the poet tell you about Miss Rosie's past? Why does she emphasize the contrast between the woman's past and her present circumstances?

3. What does the poet mean when she refers to Miss Rosie's "destruction"? What does she mean when she says, "I stand up through your destruction"?

● What is a vase for? It is for the arrangement and display of something valued for its beauty.

Gary Snyder

VASE: SEPTEMBER

Old Mrs. Kawabata
cuts down the tall spike weeds —
　　　more in two hours
than I can get done in a day.
Out of a mountain
of grass and thistle
she saved five dusty stalks
　　　of ragged wild blue flower
and put them in my kitchen in a jar.

A CLOSER LOOK

1. What part of the poem tells about something that happens on a regular basis, perhaps every fall? What part tells about something that happened on one specific occasion? (To answer this question, look at the tenses of the verbs.)

2. According to the dictionary, a weed is an "unsightly or troublesome plant." Do you think that Mrs. Kawabata and the poet would agree with this definition? Give evidence from the poem to support your answer.

3. How does Mrs. Kawabata show that she has an eye for beauty even in "worthless" objects? Does she believe that the poet shares her sense of beauty? Give evidence to support your answer.

● He says there is only one person in the world whom she really loves. Who is it?

D. H. Lawrence

INTIMATES

Don't you care for my love? she said bitterly.

I handed her the mirror, and said:
Please address these questions to the proper person!
Please make all requests to headquarters!
In all matters of emotional importance
please approach the supreme authority direct!
So I handed her the mirror.

And she would have broken it over my head,
but she caught sight of her own reflection
and that held her spell-bound for two seconds
while I fled.

A CLOSER LOOK

1. The poem tells the story of a lovers' quarrel. Whose side of the story do we hear, the man's or the woman's?

2. In the first line, the woman asks the man a question: **Don't you care that I love you?** *The man says she must ask that question of the "proper person." What person does he mean? How does he show the woman what person he means?*

3. Does he or does he not believe that the woman loves him? If not, whom does he think she loves?

• For many people, one of the memorable "firsts" in life is the first date. Gary Soto tells the story of his first date in this poem.

Gary Soto

ORANGES

The first time I walked
With a girl, I was twelve,
Cold, and weighted down
With two oranges in my jacket.
December. Frost cracking
Beneath my steps, my breath
Before me, then gone,
As I walked toward
Her house, the one whose
Porch light burned yellow
Night and day, in any weather.
A dog barked at me, until
She came out pulling
At her gloves, face bright
With rouge. I smiled,
Touched her shoulder, and led
Her down the street, across
A used car lot and a line
Of newly planted trees,
Until we were breathing
Before a drugstore. We
Entered, the tiny bell
Bringing a saleslady
Down a narrow aisle of goods.
I turned to the candies
Tiered like bleachers,
And asked what she wanted —
Light in her eyes, a smile
Starting at the corners
Of her mouth. I fingered
A nickel in my pocket,
And when she lifted a chocolate
That cost a dime,
I didn't say anything.

I took the nickel from
My pocket, then an orange,
And set them quietly on
The counter. When I looked up,
The lady's eyes met mine,
And held them, knowing
Very well what it was all
About.
                              Outside,
A few cars hissing past,
Fog hanging like old
Coats between the trees.
I took my girl's hand
In mine for two blocks,
Then released it to let
Her unwrap the chocolate.
I peeled my orange
That was so bright against
The gray of December
That, from some distance,
Someone might have thought
I was making a fire in my
hands.

A CLOSER LOOK

1. The success of a date depends mainly on how well the boy and girl play the roles that society expects them to play. For example, in this poem the girl's role includes trying to make herself look extra nice, and accepting the boy's attentions and gift. What does the boy's role include?

2. At what point in the story is the boy threatened with humiliating failure? What problem does he face and what solution does he think of? Who helps him by accepting the solution?

3. Point out some of the sensory details that help you "experience" the story in your imagination. (Two examples are "frost cracking beneath my steps" and "face bright with rouge.") What one image seems to sum up the boy's feelings of joy and satisfaction at the success of his date?

• The poet thinks of a clever new way to say, "I miss you."

Ron Padgett

LITTLE POEM

I call you on
the 'phone &
we chat, but
the way tele
is missing from
'phone is the
way it makes me
feel, wishing
the rest of
you were here.

A CLOSER LOOK

1. To show how incomplete he feels, the poet compares himself to one part of a two-part word. What does "phone" need to make it whole?

2. What does the poet need to make him whole?

3. What does the missing word-part mean? (Look it up in the dictionary if necessary.) How does that meaning apply to the poet's "missing part"?

- The poet says it doesn't matter whether he's one lover among many or one alone: he is the one who'll be true forever.

Guadalupe de Saavedra

IF YOU HEAR THAT A THOUSAND PEOPLE LOVE YOU

IF you hear that a thousand people love you
remember . . . saavedra is among them.

IF you hear that a hundred people love you
remember . . . saavedra is either in the first
  or very last row.

IF you hear that seven people love you
remember . . . saavedra is among them,
like a wednesday in the middle of the week

IF you hear that two people love you
remember . . . one of them is saavedra

IF you hear that only one person loves you
remember . . . he is saavedra

AND when you see no one else around you,
  and you find out
  that no one loves you anymore,
  then you will know for certain
  that . . . saavedra is dead.

A CLOSER LOOK

1. The poet says the same thing six times, but in six slightly different ways. (It is this combination of repetition and variation that keeps the reader interested and amused.) One of the variables that the poet uses is number: he starts with a large number (1,000) and works his way down to zero. Would the poem have been more effective or less effective if he had gone from zero to 1,000? Why?

2. *Another variable is the poet's location within the group of lovers. Find four different words or phrases that the poet uses to indicate his location. Which do you think is the most amusing?*

3. *What one point is the poet making?*

● This poem is written in the form of a dialogue between the poet and a girl with beautiful blonde hair. The hair makes her attractive to boys, so she probably considers it an asset. But the poet tells her it's a problem, and he's only half joking.

William Butler Yeats

FOR ANNE GREGORY

"Never shall a young man,
Thrown into despair
By those great honey-colored
Ramparts at your ear,
Love you for yourself alone
And not your yellow hair."

"But I can get a hair-dye
And set such color there,
Brown, or black, or carrot,
That young men in despair
May love me for myself alone
And not my yellow hair."

"I heard an old religious man
But yesternight declare
That he had found a text to prove
That only God, my dear,
Could love you for yourself alone
And not your yellow hair."

A CLOSER LOOK

1. According to the poet, what problem does Anne have?

2. In the second stanza, Anne says there is a simple solution to the problem. What is it?

3. In the third stanza, the poet tells Anne that her solution won't work. His tone is still humorous, but his thought is serious: only God, he says, can love her for her true self and not for her appearance. If Anne asked, "Why is this so?" what would the poet answer?

• "Come Hither, My Dear One" is a lyric love poem. This special type of poem originated in Europe in the early Middle Ages, when troubadours (traveling songwriters) went from castle to castle composing songs in honor of highborn ladies.

John Clare

COME HITHER, MY DEAR ONE

Come hither, my dear one, my choice one, and rare one,
    And let us be walking the meadows so fair,
Where on pilewort and daisies the eye fondly gazes,
    And the wind plays so sweet in thy bonny brown hair.

Come with thy maiden eye, lay silks and satins by;
    Come in thy russet or grey cotton gown;
Come to the meads, dear, where flags, sedge, and reeds appear,
    Rustling to soft winds and bowing low down.

Come with thy parted hair, bright eyes, and forehead bare;
    Come to the whitethorn that grows in the land;
To banks of primroses, where sweetness reposes,
    Come, love, and let us be happy again.

Come where the violet flowers, come where the morning showers
    Pearls on the primrose and speedwell so blue;
Come to that clearest brook that ever runs round the nook
    Where you and I pledged our first love so true.

A CLOSER LOOK

1. Certain ideas and themes appear over and over in lyric love poetry. See if you can find examples in this poem of the following: (a) The poet praises the beauty of the lady to whom the song is addressed. (b) The poet mentions some of the beauties of nature. (c) The poet says or implies that the simple life is better than the life of pomp and luxury.

2. Alliteration is the repetition of a sound at the beginning of two or more words in the same line. An example is the repetition of the initial "b" in "bonny brown hair." Find two more examples,

one in the second stanza and one in the fourth.

3. In each stanza, the last word in the second line rhymes with the last word in the fourth. In addition, there is internal rhyme in the first and third lines of every stanza. For example, in the first line of the first stanza, "one" rhymes with "one" (this is called identical rhyme); and in the third line "daisies" rhymes with "gazes" (this is called near-rhyme). Find the internal rhymes in the other three stanzas of the poem.

● Do not look for meaning in this poem — you won't find any. What you will find is a melodious, rhythmic chant based on the word "love." When you read the poem aloud, as you should do, pronounce the Italian phrase "dove sta amore" like this: DOH-veh stah eh-MOR-eh. It means "where lies love."

Lawrence Ferlinghetti

WHERE LIES LOVE

Dove sta amore
Where lies love
Dove sta amore
Here lies love
The ring dove love
In lyrical delight
Hear love's hillsong
Love's true will song
Love's low plainsong
Too sweet painsong
In passages of night
Dove sta amore
Here lies love
The ring dove love
Dove sta amore
Here lies love.

A CLOSER LOOK

1. See if you can find a pattern in the way the lines of the poem are arranged. (Hint: There are three groups, each held together by rhyming words at the ends of the lines.)

2. What are some of the words that the poet included because of their associations with love? ("Dove" is one.)

3. It's possible that the poet is making fun of popular love poems and love songs that have silly meanings or no meaning at all. If you can, give an example of such a poem or song.

● The young wife of a Chinese river-merchant writes a letter to her husband, who is away on business. In the letter, she tells her husband how much she misses him.

Li Po

THE RIVER-MERCHANT'S WIFE: A LETTER

While my hair was still cut straight across my forehead
I played about the front gate, pulling flowers.
You came by on bamboo stilts, playing horse;
You walked about my seat, playing with blue plums.
And we went on living in the village of Chokan:
Two small people, without dislike or suspicion.

At fourteen I married My Lord you.
I never laughed, being bashful.
Lowering my head, I looked at the wall.
Called to, a thousand times, I never looked back.

At fifteen I stopped scowling,
I desired my dust to be mingled with yours
Forever and forever and forever.
Why should I climb the look-out?

At sixteen you departed,
You went into far Ku-to-Yen by the river of swirling eddies,
And you have been gone five months.
The monkeys make sorrowful noise overhead.
You dragged your feet when you went out.
By the gate now, the moss is grown, the different mosses
Too deep to clear them away!
The leaves fall early this autumn, in wind.
The paired butterflies are already yellow with August
Over the grass in the west garden —
They hurt me.
I grow older.
If you are coming down through the narrows of the river Kiang,
Please let me know beforehand,
And I will come out to meet you,
As far as Cho-fu-Sa.

(Translation by Ezra Pound)

A CLOSER LOOK

1. The poem is divided into four sections, one for each of the stages in the young woman's relationship with her husband. The first line in each section tells how old she was at that stage. What were her feelings in the first and second stages?

2. The expression "climb the look-out" is a metaphor for "look for someone to love." At what stage did the woman realize that she had found someone to love?

3. Find two or three images in the poem that convey the woman's sadness and loneliness.

● Usually food is just food: a source of vitamins and minerals. But sometimes it becomes a symbol that offers a different kind of nourishment.

Cornelius Eady

MY CHILDHOOD IN GREASE

Nick Tahous
is the
greatest
greasy spoon
in western new york
and I was weaned
on his
texas hots and hamburgers.

Nick's first place was
a little shop
with sawdust on the floor
where they spoke
the first foreign language I ever heard.
I suspected
the sauce's secret
was
in greek.

my father and I
would seal any adventure together
with a visit
to Nick's.
he'd cautiously admit he loved me
with a ritual of hamburgers
and cokes.

love and grease has followed me through the years.

today
when I desire to show anyone I love them
I cook them something
and I don't spare
the oil.

A CLOSER LOOK

1. A "greasy spoon" is a restaurant where many of the dishes are fried in oil. What greasy spoon did the poet sometimes visit when he was a boy? Who took him there? What did he eat?

2. Why did the boy associate greasy food with love? Now that he is an adult, are the two still connected in his mind? What lines give you the answer?

3. What part of the poem contains a pun? What is the pun?

● Harlem, a section of New York City, is the place where many black musicians, artists, and writers did some of their most important work.

Langston Hughes

HARLEM NIGHT SONG

Come,
Let us roam the night together
Singing.

I love you.

Across
The Harlem roof-tops
Moon is shining.

Night sky is blue.
Stars are great drops
Of golden dew.

Down the street
A band is playing.

I love you.

Come.
Let us roam the night together
Singing.

A CLOSER LOOK

1. Many songs have a refrain: a phrase or series of phrases that is repeated at regular intervals. This song seems to have two refrains. What are they?

2. Find three images in the poem that give the scene an almost magical quality.

• Most poets writing today ignore the sonnet. They feel that its strict rules, which call for exactly fourteen lines with a certain rhythm and rhyme scheme, cramp their imaginations. But the limitations of the sonnet form didn't daunt Shakespeare — he overcame them successfully 154 times.

William Shakespeare

SONNET 29

When, in disgrace with Fortune and men's eyes,
I all alone beweep my outcast state,
And trouble deaf heaven with my bootless cries,
And look upon myself and curse my fate,
Wishing me like to one more rich in hope,
Featur'd like him, like him with friends possess'd,
Desiring this man's art and that man's scope,
With what I most enjoy contented least;
Yet in these thoughts myself almost despising,
Haply I think on thee; and then my state,
Like to the lark at break of day arising
From sullen earth, sings hymns at heaven's gate;
    For thy sweet love rememb'red such wealth brings
    That then I scorn to change my state with kings.

A CLOSER LOOK

1. In the first eight lines of Sonnet 29, Shakespeare describes the mood of despair that comes over him from time to time. He finds himself unlucky and unpopular, and he compares himself unfavorably with other men. According to the poet, in what ways are these men more fortunate than he?

2. In the last six lines of the poem the poet tells what happens when "haply" (by chance) a certain thought comes to his mind. What is that thought? How does it affect the poet's (and the poem's) mood?

● This English translation of an Italian sonnet is not bound by the rules of the sonnet form. Its lines are unrhymed and have the irregular rhythm of casual speech. In fact, they give the impression that the speaker of the poem and his friend Guido are just sitting around and chatting idly about their dreams and wishes.

Dante Alighieri

SONETTO

Guido, I wish that you and Lapo and I
Were carried off by magic
And put in a boat, which, every time there was wind,
Would sail on the ocean exactly where we wanted.
In this way storms and other dangerous weather
Wouldn't be able to harm us,
And I wish that, since we all were of one mind,
We'd go on wanting more and more to be together.
And I wish that Vanna and Lagia too
And the girl whose name on the list is number thirty
Were put in the boat by the magician too
And that we all did nothing but talk about love,
And I wish that they were just as glad to be there
As I believe the three of us would be.

(Translation by Kenneth Koch)

A CLOSER LOOK

1. Does the speaker think he has any chance of getting his wish? Find evidence in the poem to support your answer.

2. The speaker mentions three girls, two by name and one by reference to her place on a list. Which of the three do you think are the girlfriends of Guido and Lapo? Which do you think is the one the speaker loves?

3. Why does the speaker avoid saying the name that is number thirty on the list?

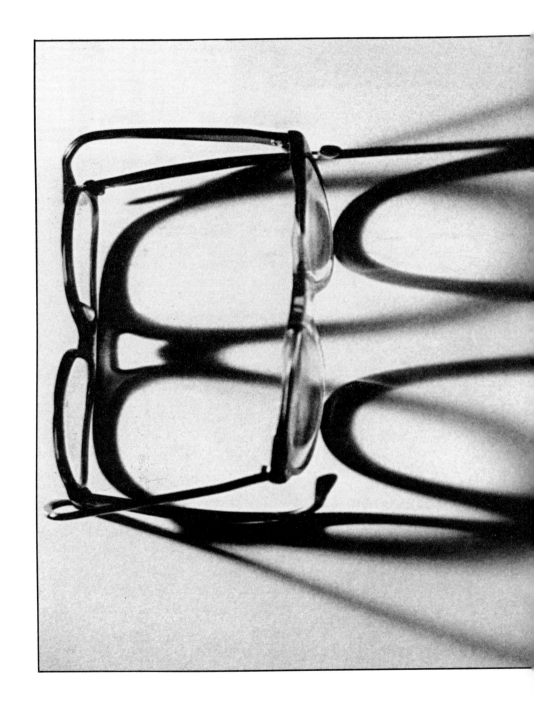

SEEING AND FEELING

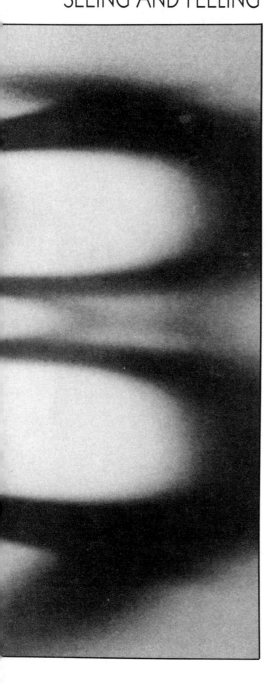

● In "Foul Shot," Edwin Hoey uses a slow-motion technique to describe the last two seconds of a tied-up basketball game. With this technique, he conveys the atmosphere of tension and anticipation so vividly that you feel as if you were right there in the gym, holding your breath as the crucial play unfolds.

Edwin Hoey

FOUL SHOT

With two 60's stuck on the scoreboard
And two seconds hanging on the clock,
The solemn boy in the center of eyes,
Squeezed by silence,
Seeks out the line with his feet,
Soothes his hands along his uniform,
Gently drums the ball against the floor,
Then measures the waiting net,
Raises the ball on his right hand,
Balances it with his left,
Calms it with fingertips,
Breathes,
Crouches,
Waits,
And then through a stretching of stillness,
Nudges it upward.

The ball
Slides up and out,
Lands,
Leans,
Wobbles,
Wavers,
Hesitates,
Exasperates,
Plays it coy
Until every face begs with unsounding
screams —
And then

                    And then

                              And then,

Right before ROAR-UP,
Dives down and through.

A CLOSER LOOK

1. *Time seems suspended as we read the poem; the "foul shot"*
seems to last an eternity. In reality, how much time do you
suppose the action takes?

2. *Why does the poet put each detail on a separate line?*

3. *Imagine that you are part of the crowd, watching the game.*
Reread the last stanza of the poem. What will happen next?

● The poem below shows how an emotion, such as fear, can spread from person to person in a group.

Charles Simic

FEAR

Fear passes from man to man
Unknowing,
As one leaf passes its shudder
To another.

All at once the whole tree is trembling
And there is no sign of wind.

A CLOSER LOOK

1. According to the poem, do people know what is happening when "fear passes from man to man"? Which word in the poem gives you the answer?

2. In the second stanza, the poet is comparing a trembling tree to a group of frightened people. He tells us that there is no reason for the tree to be trembling. What conclusion do you think he wants us to draw about the people?

● While waiting to have his picture taken by a famous artist, the poet does some "picture-taking" of his own.

Allen Ginsberg

FOURTH FLOOR, DAWN, UP ALL NIGHT WRITING LETTERS

Pigeons shake their wings on the copper church roof
out my window across the street, a bird perched on the cross
surveys the city's blue-gray clouds. Larry Rivers
'll come at 10 A.M. and take my picture. I'm taking
your picture, pigeons. I'm writing you down, Dawn.
I'm immortalizing your exhaust, Avenue A bus.
O Thought, now you'll have to think the same thing forever!

(New York, June 7, 1980, 6:48)

A CLOSER LOOK

1. What does the poet mean when he says, "I'm taking your picture, pigeons"? What is he really doing?

2. Find the four places where the poet uses direct address. To whom or what is he talking in each case? Why is that amusing?

3. What will happen at 10 A.M.? In what way is taking a picture like writing a poem?

4. In the last line, Ginsberg tells the poem (the "Thought") that it will be the same forever. How will the picture of the poet be like the poem he has just written?

● The poet uses a metaphor to create a visual image of a passenger boat.

Eric Berger

THE FERRY

Churning white water
The huge turtle
Lumbers into the bay.
Gulls,
Wheeling, squealing,
Spear scraps,
Follow the wake —
Wings awash in sunlight.

A CLOSER LOOK

1. The poet refers to the ferry as a turtle. Why is this a good metaphor? What does it tell us about the way a ferry moves?

2. The poet contrasts the ferry with the gulls. What words does he use to describe the movement of each?

● Using words of light and color, the poet paints a picture of a particular day in his life. He doesn't say when it was, and he doesn't tell what happened. But he shows us very clearly how he felt about that day.

Donald Justice

SONG

Morning opened
Like a rose,
And the snow on the roof
Rose-color took.
Oh, how the street
Toward light did leap!
And the lamps went out.
Brightness fell down
From the steep clock
To the row of shops
And rippled the bricks
Like the scales of a fish,
And all that day
Was a fairy tale
Told once in a while
To a good child.

A CLOSER LOOK

1. Instead of saying that there was a rosy light in the sky as the sun came up, the poet says that "morning opened like a rose." What ideas or feelings do we associate with roses? Why does the poet show us a bud opening rather than a fully opened flower?

2. Find one or two other images that show how fresh and rarely beautiful the morning seemed to the poet.

3. You've heard the expression "It was like a fairy tale." What does it mean? The poet says the day was like a specific kind of fairy tale: the kind that's told to a good child. How might a fairy tale told to a good child differ from one told to a bad child?

4. How often does the poet (or any person) have a good-child-fairy-tale day? What phrase gives you the answer?

• The third week moon, a full moon, appears in about the middle of the four-week lunar cycle. The title "Late Moon" probably refers to the time of night that the poet is describing.

Robert Bly

LATE MOON

The third week moon reaches its light over my father's farm,
half of it dark now, in the west that eats it away.
The earth has rocks in it that hum at early dawn.
As I turn to go in, I see my shadow reach for the latch.

A CLOSER LOOK

1. The poet has finished his early-morning chores and is about to go back inside the farmhouse. He pauses to look out over the moonlit fields. Where is he standing?

2. The second line tells us that the moon is setting. What does the poet mean when he says that the west "eats it away"?

3. In which line does the poet tell us that the earth is beginning to awaken?

4. What happens in the last line?

● One thing leads to another, and in the poem below we see how a simple act can set off a chain reaction.

Jon Goldman

THE SIGHT

Sixteen stories down
people are playing
tennis,
hitting,
running,
a dog drinks
from a puddle
which a boy
bikes through
wetting the dog
who barks
causing a baby
to cry,
the mother says
hush,
hush

A CLOSER LOOK

1. Is the poet observing or participating in the scene described? How do you know?

2. Which event sets the chain reaction in motion?

3. "The Sight" is the poet's report of a series of events. Which part of the report involves another sense besides sight? How accurate do you think this part probably is? Explain your answer.

● An omen is a prophetic sign: an object or event that is believed to foretell the future. See if you can find an omen in this poem by the Senegalese writer Birago Diop.

Birago Diop

OMEN

A naked sun — a yellow sun
A sun all naked at early dawn
Pours waves of gold over the bank
Of the river of yellow.

A naked sun — a white sun
A sun all naked and white
Pours waves of silver
Over the river of white.

A naked sun — a red sun
A sun all naked and red
Pours waves of red blood
Over the river of red.

(Translated from the French by Moore and Beier)

A CLOSER LOOK

1. We know that the yellow sun is the rising sun, and we can conclude that the red sun is the setting sun. At what time of day can we assume the white sun appears?

2. Which word in the last stanza lets us know that the red sun is an omen of something bad?

● The Bible tells the story of how the life of the infant Moses was saved when his mother hid him among the bulrushes (tall, grasslike weeds) on the banks of the Nile River. The daughter of the Pharaoh (the Egyptian king) found Moses and took him home with her to live in the palace.

Samuel Menashe

REEDS RISE FROM WATER

Reeds rise from water

rippling under my eyes
Bulrushes tuft the shore

At every instant I expect
what is hidden everywhere

A CLOSER LOOK

1. *What story is the poet thinking of as he looks at the reeds and bulrushes?*

2. *The poet keeps expecting that he, too, will find something — not a baby in the bulrushes, of course, but perhaps something equally extraordinary. He is constantly on the alert to discover "what is hidden everywhere" in the world around him. What do you think is hidden everywhere? What is waiting to be discovered? (There are no right or wrong answers to this question. Just use your imagination.)*

● We all know that a genius is an extremely intelligent person. But the word can also be applied to any person who sees something that others don't see.

Charles Bukowski

I MET A GENIUS

I met a genius on the train
today
about 6 years old.
he sat beside me
and as the train
ran down along the coast
we came to the ocean
and then he looked at me
and said,
it's not pretty.

it was the first time I'd
realized
that.

A CLOSER LOOK

1. Like many people, the speaker in this poem has ideas that he never questions. For example, he has always assumed that the ocean is pretty. What makes him question this idea?

2. Do you think the speaker will begin to question other assumptions that he holds? Why or why not?

3. The poem suggests that there is a difference between the way a child looks at the world and the way an adult looks at it. What is the difference?

● Nantucket is a large island off the coast of Massachusetts. Formerly a center of the whaling industry, it is now a picturesque resort that attracts many visitors, especially in the summer. The speaker in this poem may or may not be a visitor. All we know is that he looks into a room and describes what he sees.

William Carlos Williams

NANTUCKET

Flowers through the window
lavender and yellow

changed by white curtains —
Smell of cleanliness —

Sunshine of late afternoon —
on the glass tray

a glass pitcher, the tumbler
turned down, by which

a key is lying — And the
immaculate white bed.

A CLOSER LOOK

1. *How are the lavender and yellow flowers "changed" by white curtains?*

2. *The poet provides clues that let us know the room is in a hotel or a rooming house. What are the clues?*

3. *Is the room vacant or occupied? Find evidence in the poem to support your answer.*

● Robert Wallace captures one of those moments in a baseball game when a team's coordinated moves are so quick, so graceful, and so effective that they deserve to be called "pure poetry."

Robert Wallace

THE DOUBLE-PLAY

In his sea lit
distance, the pitcher winding
like a clock about to chime comes down with

the ball, hit
sharply, under the artificial
banks of arc-lights, bounds like a vanishing string

over the green
to the shortstop magically
scoops to his right whirling above his invisible

shadows
in the dust redirects
its flight to the running poised second baseman

pirouettes
leaping, above the slide, to throw
from mid-air, across the colored tightened interval

to the leaning-
out first baseman ends the dance
drawing it disappearing into his long brown glove

stretches. What
is too swift for deception
is final, lost, among the loosened figures

jogging off the field
(the pitcher walks), casual
in the space where the poem has happened.

A CLOSER LOOK

1. Approximately how many separate actions are included in this description of a double-play? Why does the poet run all the actions together in one sentence?

2. At what point in the poem do we know that the inning is over?

3. The phrase "What is too swift for deception" refers to the incredible feat that the poet has just witnessed: the double-play. Now that the play is over, how do the players appear? Contrast the way they appear now with the way they appeared during the double-play.

● Here's a clue to the meaning of this poem: The "listener" mentioned in the last stanza is the snow man of the title. The poem is about the difference between the snow man's view of his surroundings and a person's view of the same surroundings. The snow man does not see the snow and ice or hear the wind. The person not only sees the snow and ice and hears the wind but also thinks about what they "mean." Thoughts of cold, hunger, or death — often linked in the human mind with the thought of winter — make the person see things in the scene that aren't actually there.

Wallace Stevens

THE SNOW MAN

One must have a mind of winter
To regard the frost and the boughs
Of the pine-trees crusted with snow;

And have been cold a long time
To behold the junipers shagged with ice,
The spruces rough in the distant glitter

Of the January sun; and not to think
Of any misery in the sound of the wind,
In the sound of a few leaves,

Which is the sound of the land
Full of the same wind
That is blowing in the same bare place

For the listener, who listens in the snow,
And, nothing himself, beholds
Nothing that is not there and the nothing that is.

A CLOSER LOOK

1. What do you think the poet means by "a mind of winter" in the first line? Who in the poem has a mind of winter?

2. The snow man sees "nothing that is not there." How does that make him different from human beings?

● The haiku is a type of poem that originated in Japan. Because the rules of the form limit the writer to a very few words, he or she has to make every word count. When successful, a haiku sketches a vivid picture that awakens a feeling or starts a train of thought in the reader's mind. Here are two examples by one of the greatest Japanese masters of the form.

Basho

TWO HAIKU

The temple bell stops —
        but the sound keeps coming
            out of the flowers.

A crow is perched
        upon a leafless withered bough —
          the autumn dusk.

A CLOSER LOOK

1. In the first haiku, what do you think the flowers might look like? What shape might they have?

2. Whatever their shape, flowers can't ring, so the poet doesn't really hear the sound of the temple bell coming out of them. However, the poet might perceive other kinds of beauty in the flowers, and these might blend in his mind with the beautiful sound of the bell. To what senses might the flowers appeal?

3. The second haiku points out details of a scene that give it a certain atmosphere or mood. What season of the year is it? What time of day is it? Is the scene dark or light? What do the crow and the dead branch of a tree make you think of? How does the poem make you feel?

● In this haiku, Ezra Pound sees a crowd in a Paris subway station and makes a startling comparison.

Ezra Pound

IN A STATION OF THE METRO

The apparition of these faces in the crowd;
Petals on a wet, black bough.

A CLOSER LOOK

1. Which is the poet talking about, the faces themselves or the vision he saw as he looked at the faces?

2. Try substituting each of these words for the word "apparition" in the first line: "sight," "look," "appearance." Why is "apparition" the best word to use in this phrase? (You may want to look the word up in your dictionary.)

3. Which part of the scene looks like petals to the poet? Which part looks like a wet, black bough? What do you think makes the bough look black? What makes it look wet? (Your answer to this last question can be just a guess.)

● In this poem Charles Reznikoff makes us look at a subway station in a new way.

Charles Reznikoff

UNTITLED POEM

Walk about the subway station
in a grove of steel pillars;
how their knobs, the rivet-heads —
unlike those of oaks —
are regularly placed:
how barren the ground is
except here and there on the platform
a flat black fungus
that was chewing-gum.

A CLOSER LOOK

1. The poet compares the subway station to a grove (group) of oak trees. What similarities between these two places does he find?

2. What differences does he find?

3. Which place does the poet prefer, the subway station or the grove of oak trees? How do you know this?

● How does it feel to be driving alone through the small, quiet hours of the night when the rest of the world is sleeping?

Donald Justice

POEM TO BE READ AT 3 A.M.

Excepting the diner
On the outskirts
The town of Ladora
At 3 a.m.
Was dark but
For my headlights
And up in
One second story room
A single light
Where someone
Was sick or
Perhaps reading
As I drove past
At seventy
Not thinking
This poem
Is for whoever
Had the light on.

A CLOSER LOOK

1. How do you think the poet felt as he drove through the dark, quiet town?

2. The poet noticed a "single light" in one room. Did he think about the person in that room as he drove past it? Or did he think about the person later on? How do you know?

3. How do we know that the poet came to feel a sense of kinship with the person in the room? On what fact was their kinship based?

● Traditional Chinese philosophy holds that the human race is a part of nature. Only when human beings are aware of their place in nature are they fully alive. In this poem, a journey through nature takes the poet to a place of quiet contemplation where he is able to discover the deepest part of himself.

Wang Wei

A GREEN STREAM

I have come on the River of Yellow Flowers,
Borne by the current of a green stream
Rounding ten thousand turns through the mountains
To journey less than a hundred li.
Rapids hum on scattered stones,
Light is dim in the close pines,
The surface of an inlet sways with nut-horns,
Weeds are lush along the banks.
Down in my heart I have always been clear
As this clarity of waters.
Oh, to remain on a broad flat rock
And cast my fishing line forever.

(Translation by Witter Bynner and Kiang Kang-hu)

A CLOSER LOOK

1. The poet starts by describing the beauties of nature. At what point in the poem does he begin to talk about the deepest part of himself?

2. What does the poet mean when he says, "Down in my heart I have always been clear"? What word in this sentence implies that at times he may not have appeared or acted "clear"?

3. In the last two lines, the poet is saying that he doesn't want to return to the everyday world. Why not? What is he afraid he will lose if he doesn't remain in contact with nature?

• The Piazza di Spagna (Spanish Plaza) in Rome is at the foot of a magnificent marble stairway called the Spanish Steps. The steps are usually teeming with people, so it is significant that the action of the poem takes place in the early morning.

Richard Wilbur

PIAZZA DI SPAGNA, EARLY MORNING

I can't forget
How she stood at the top of that long marble stair
Amazed, and then with a sleepy pirouette
Went dancing slowly down to the fountain-quieted square;

Nothing upon her face
But some impersonal loneliness — not then a girl,
But as a reverie of the place
A called-for falling glide and whirl;

As when a leaf, petal, or thin chip
Is drawn to the falls of a pool and, circling a moment above
Rides over the lip —
Perfectly beautiful, perfectly ignorant of it.

A CLOSER LOOK

1. What is the main action of the poem?

2. In the second stanza, the poet says that, in his mind, the girl ceased to be a girl and became a reverie (daydream) of the place. How do we know that the place seemed lonely to the poet? Why did the "falling glide and whirl" seem to be a called-for (necessary) part of the daydream?

3. What does the poet compare the girl's motion to?

4. Was the girl aware that she was part of a beautiful and unforgettable picture? How do you know?

• An ode is a poem in praise of something or someone. In this ode, the Nobel Prize-winning poet Pablo Neruda praises something that is usually considered quite ordinary: a pair of socks.

Pablo Neruda

ODE TO MY SOCKS

Maru Mori brought me
a pair
of socks
which she knitted herself
with her sheepherder's hands,
two socks as soft
as rabbits.
I slipped my feet
into them
as though into
two
cases
knitted
with threads of
twilight
and goatskin.
Violent socks,
my feet were
two fish made
of wool,
two long sharks,
sea-blue, shot
through
by one golden thread,
two immense blackbirds,
two cannons:

my feet
were honored
in this way
by
these
heavenly
socks.
They were
so handsome
for the first time
my feet seemed to me
unacceptable
like two decrepit
firemen, firemen
unworthy
of that woven
fire,
of those glowing
socks.

Nevertheless
I resisted
the sharp temptation
to save them somewhere
as schoolboys
keep
fireflies,
as learned men
collect
sacred texts,
I resisted
the mad impulse
to put them

into a golden
cage
and each day give them
birdseed
and pieces of pink melon.
Like explorers
in the jungle who hand
over the very rare
green deer
to the spit
and eat it
with remorse,
I stretched out
my feet
and pulled on
the magnificent
socks
and then my shoes.
The moral
of my ode is this:
beauty is twice
beauty
and what is good is doubly
good
when it is a matter of two
socks
made of wool
in winter.

(Translation by Robert Bly)

A CLOSER LOOK

1. What does the poet compare his feet to after he puts his new socks on?

2. What is he tempted to do with the socks? What reason would he have for doing these things with the socks? In what way is he like explorers in the jungle who kill and eat a rare animal?

3. Is the poet the kind of person to whom you would enjoy giving a gift? Explain your answer.

● This riddle-poem contains four clues, each starting with the words "I am . . ." and the name of an animal. Read the clues and then answer the question "What am I?" (Hint: Each clue points to something associated with the animal, not the animal itself.)

Brian Swann

UNTITLED POEM

I am the old wolf
pricking bare tundra
with my throat
pulling the pack together
as they join in
after my third howl

I am the bearded seal
playing the same air
over and over
while the Eskimo
puts his ear to the paddle
and listens

I am the whale
distilling my bulk
to the thin perfect pitch
of bird-song

I am the lark
that rises straight up
like a smoke-column
over moor and meadow
and am heard
after I am seen
no more

A CLOSER LOOK

1. *What are all four animals doing?*

2. *What one thing is associated with all four animals?*

3. *What is the answer to the riddle?*

• The poem on this page might be called a collaborative poem because it was written by a group of people working together. The authors were challenged to take a common object and think up imaginative new ways of perceiving or using it.

Anonymous Group

THE PINEAPPLE EVENT POEM

1. Cut the pineapple in half and wear the two halves as earmuffs on a cold winter day.
2. Peel the skins off 100 pineapples, and glue them down to the floor as tiles.
3. Cut out five of the little round lozenges on the pineapple's skin, and sew them on your jacket as buttons.
4. Look at the pineapple. It looks like the torch in the Statue of Liberty.
5. Feel the pineapple. It feels like ten mosquitoes are biting your hand.

A CLOSER LOOK

1. Do you think the authors of this poem had fun writing it? Why or why not?

2. Do you think that writing this kind of poem is a good mental exercise? Why or why not?

UNIT V
TAKING PART

● Looking forward to an experience can be almost as special and exciting as the experience itself. In this poem, the speaker looks forward to the traditional feasting and dancing that bind his Native American community together.

Alonzo Lopez

CELEBRATION

I shall dance tonight.
When the dusk comes crawling,
There will be dancing
       and feasting.
I shall dance with the others
       in circles,
          in leaps,
             in stomps.
Laughter and talk
       will weave into the night,
Among the fires
       of my people,
Games will be played
And I shall be
       a part of it.

A CLOSER LOOK

1. The poet writes about a celebration that is still in the future. What mood does this create? How would the mood of the poem have been different if the poet had written about a celebration in the past?

2. Does the speaker expect to feel a sense of belonging as he joins in the celebration? What lines give you the answer?

● Carl Sandburg was a "public poet" who loved to perform before large audiences. Besides reading and reciting his own poems, he would also sing folksongs, accompanying himself on his guitar. As you read "Stars, Songs, Faces," think about how it would sound if read out loud.

Carl Sandburg

STARS, SONGS, FACES

Gather the stars if you wish it so.
Gather the songs and keep them.
Gather the faces of women.
Gather for keeping years and years.
    And then . . .
Loosen your hands, let go and say good-bye.
    Let the stars and songs go.
    Let the faces and years go.
    Loosen your hands and say good-bye.

A CLOSER LOOK

1. We can't actually gather the stars. What do you think the word "gather" means in this poem?

2. Identify some of the words and phrases that are repeated in this poem. What effect do the repetitions have on the sound and rhythm of the poem?

3. The repeated words and phrases are arranged in two groups, and these groups make up two sections of the poem. Which lines are in the first section? Which lines are in the second section? What main idea is expressed in each section?

4. What advice is the poet giving us in this poem? Do you think it is good advice? Why or why not?

● A blessing is an expression of kind good-will. When the one who blesses has no motive but love, and the one who is blessed is grateful, the blessing gives joy to both.

James Wright

A BLESSING

Just off the highway to Rochester, Minnesota,
Twilight bounds softly forth on the grass.
And the eyes of those two Indian ponies
Darken with kindness.
They have come gladly out of the willows
To welcome my friend and me.
We step over the barbed wire into the pasture
Where they have been grazing all day, alone.
They ripple tensely, they can hardly contain their happiness
That we have come.
They bow shyly as wet swans. They love each other.
There is no loneliness like theirs.
At home once more,
They begin munching the young tufts of spring in the darkness.
I would like to hold the slenderer one in my arms,
For she has walked over to me
And nuzzled my left hand.
She is black and white,
Her mane falls wild on her forehead,
And the light breeze moves me to caress her long ear
That is as delicate as the skin over a girl's wrist.
Suddenly I realize
That if I stepped out of my body I would break
Into blossom.

A CLOSER LOOK

1. Why do the ponies come out of the willows and come to the fence when they see the two people? Why do the speaker and his friend step over the fence?

2. According to the speaker, what emotions do the ponies feel? What evidence does he see that they feel these emotions?

3. What is the blessing? Who gives it? Who receives it? How does the receiver respond?

• The poem below might be called a "found" poem. Jerome Rothenberg put it together out of statements he found in a magazine article about the Kwakiutl Indians of the Pacific Northwest. The article described some of the activities that the Indians enjoyed at their traditional potlatches, or feasts. The poet selected statements about gifts and giving, and turned them into a set of instructions for a "gift event."

Jerome Rothenberg

GIFT EVENT II

1. Start by giving away different glass bowls.
2. Have everyone give everyone else a glass bowl.
3. Give away handkerchiefs and soap.
4. Give away a sack of clams.
5. Give away pigs and geese and chickens, or pretend to do so.
6. Pretend to talk Chinese and give something away.
7. Make a narrow place at the entrance of a house and put a line across it that you have to stoop under to get in.
8. Hang the line with all sorts of pots and pans that make a big noise.
9. Give away these pans while saying things like "Here is a pan worth $100, and here's one worth $200."
10. Give everyone a new name.
11. Give the newborn child a name.

A CLOSER LOOK

1. The article from which the poet got his information said that the Kwakiutl Indians had two kinds of potlatch. The first kind was an elaborate feast at which the host gave away lavish gifts to show how rich he was. The second kind was a play potlatch at which people only pretended to give things away, or gave away inexpensive or leftover items. Do you think that "Gift Event II" is about a real potlatch or a play potlatch? Explain your answer.

2. If you follow the instructions in this poem, what gifts will you actually give? What gifts will you only pretend to give? Which step lets you choose between giving and pretending?

• You are about to have your "First Lesson" in meditation. In alternating lines of this poem, the master (the poet) will pose a challenge and the pupil (you) will reply. To reply correctly, you must keep your mind relaxed but focused (that's what meditation is about). Now pay attention, and see how well you can do.

James Tate

FIRST LESSON

This is a meditation:
a snake with legs,
a one-legged snake,
a snake with wings,
a one-winged snake,
a rat with sparks,
a fiery rat,
a rat that sings,
a star rat,
a horse that explodes,
an atomic horse,
a horse that melts,
an ice horse,
a bee that flies through concrete,
a pneumatic bee,
a bee that lifts buildings,
the world's strongest bee,
a tree that eats the noses off children,
a bad tree,
a tree that grows inward until it is a dot,
a hill of dots that eats lots of children
(you are not meditating).

A CLOSER LOOK

1. *The poem follows a certain pattern. What is that pattern?*

2. *Which witty reply do you like best? Why?*

3. *Why does the last reply show that "you are not meditating"? Why is the reply incorrect? Compare it with the earlier replies that the master accepted and explain how it differs.*

PLACES NEAR AND FAR

● Louis Simpson lives in Long Island, New York, far north of the Caribbean island where he was born. The poem below seems to be his answer to the question "Is this where I belong?" or "Is this the life I was meant to live?"

Louis Simpson

CHIMNEYS

These bare brown trunks and branches
are my destiny. Destiny fits
always — no doubt about it.
There can be no such thing as a life
that wasn't meant for the person who has it.

Every day I walk in the lane
to the cliff from where there's a view
of the harbor spread out, the town
and, on the far shore, the three chimneys
of the Long Island Lighting Company.

One way to live is to tell stories:

"Once upon a time there were three chimneys —
two with red and white rings around them.
The third was considerably shorter
and painted a plain brown."

A CLOSER LOOK

1. In the first stanza, the poet describes the trees he sees around him on Long Island. Judging from this description, how do you think he feels about his life there?

2. The poet seems to be saying that destiny (fate) controls our lives. Do you agree with this idea? Tell why you agree or disagree.

3. The poet says, "One way to live is to tell stories." Explain how making up a story can (a) help a person understand life; (b) give a person a feeling of being in control; (c) give a person a chance to "escape" from reality for a while.

● When seen in the western sky around sunset, the planet Venus is called the evening star. The planet is named for the goddess of love in Roman mythology. According to one myth, the divinely beautiful Venus had neither father nor mother; she simply rose one day from the waves of the sea. A famous painting by Botticelli shows her standing on a seashell.

James Wright

TO THE EVENING STAR: CENTRAL MINNESOTA

Under the water tower at the edge of town
A huge Airedale ponders a long ripple
In the grass fields beyond.
Miles off, a whole grove silently
Flies up into the darkness.
One light comes on in the sky,
One lamp on the prairie.

Beautiful daylight of the body, your hands carry seashells.
West of this wide plain,
Animals wilder than ours
Come down from the green mountains in the darkness.
Now they can see you, they know
The open meadows are safe.

A CLOSER LOOK

1. In the first stanza the poet paints a picture of a Minnesota landscape at dusk. What two images tell you that the land is flat and empty of buildings? What is the "one light" that "comes on" (becomes visible) when the sky is dark?

2. To whom is the poet speaking in the first line of the second stanza? How do you know?

3. What sign tells wild animals that it's safe to come into the open meadows? What sign tells lovers that it's safe to meet?

● Sometimes it's hard for a person to concentrate on his work, especially when the work is boring. His mind keeps drifting off to some other place where he'd rather be.

John Ashbery

THE INSTRUCTION MANUAL

As I sit looking out of the window of the building
I wish I did not have to write the instruction manual on the uses
    of a new metal.
I look down into the street and see people, each walking with an
    inner peace,
And envy them — they are so far away from me!
Not one of them has to worry about getting out this manual on
    schedule.
And, as my way is, I begin to dream, resting my elbows on the
    desk and leaning out of the window a little,
Of dim Guadalajara! City of rose-colored flowers!
City I wanted most to see, and most did not see, in Mexico!
But I fancy I see, under the press of having to write the
    instruction manual,
Your public square, city, with its elaborate little bandstand!
The band is playing *Scheherazade* by Rimsky-Korsakov.
Around stand the flower girls, handing out rose- and lemon-
    colored flowers,
Each attractive in her rose-and-blue striped dress (Oh! such
    shades of rose and blue),
And nearby is the little white booth where women in green serve
    you green and yellow fruit.
The couples are parading; everyone is in a holiday mood.
First, leading the parade, is a dapper fellow
Clothed in deep blue. On his head sits a white hat
And he wears a mustache, which has been trimmed for the
    occasion.
His dear one, his wife, is young and pretty; her shawl is rose,
    pink, and white.

142

Her slippers are patent leather, in the American fashion,
And she carries a fan, for she is modest, and does not want the
    crowd to see her face too often.
But everybody is so busy with his wife or loved one
I doubt they would notice the mustachioed man's wife.
Here come the boys! They are skipping and throwing little things
    on the sidewalk
Which is made of gray tile. One of them, a little older, has a
    toothpick in his teeth.
He is silenter than the rest, and affects not to notice the pretty
    young girls in white.
But his friends notice them, and shout their jeers at the laughing
    girls.
Yet soon all this will cease, with the deepening of their years,
And love bring each to the parade grounds for another reason.
But I have lost sight of the young fellow with the toothpick.
Wait — there he is — on the other side of the bandstand,
Secluded from his friends, in earnest talk with a young girl
Of fourteen or fifteen. I try to hear what they are saying
But it seems they are just mumbling something — shy words of
    love, probably.
She is slightly taller than he, and looks quietly down into his
    sincere eyes.
She is wearing white. The breeze ruffles her long fine black hair
    against her olive cheek.
Obviously she is in love. The boy, the young boy with the
    toothpick, he is in love too;
His eyes show it. Turning from this couple,
I see there is an intermission in the concert.
The paraders are resting and sipping drinks through straws
(The drinks are dispensed from a large glass crock by a lady in
    dark blue),
And the musicians mingle among them, in their creamy white
    uniforms, and talk
About the weather, perhaps, or how their kids are doing at
    school.

Let us take this opportunity to tiptoe into one of the side streets.
Here you may see one of those white houses with green trim
That are so popular here. Look — I told you!

It is cool and dim inside, but the patio is sunny.
An old woman in gray sits there, fanning herself with a palm leaf
fan.
She welcomes us to her patio, and offers us a cooling drink.
"My son is in Mexico City," she says. "He would welcome you
too
If he were here. But his job is with a bank there.
Look, here is a photograph of him."
And a dark-skinned lad with pearly teeth grins out at us from the
worn leather frame.
We thank her for her hospitality, for it is getting late
And we must catch a view of the city, before we leave, from a
good high place.
That church tower will do — the faded pink one, there against
the fierce blue of the sky. Slowly we enter.
The caretaker, an old man dressed in brown and gray, asks us
how long we have been in the city, and how we like it here.
His daughter is scrubbing the steps — she nods to us as we pass
into the tower.
Soon we have reached the top, and the whole network of the city
extends before us.
There is the rich quarter, with its houses of pink and white, and
its crumbling, leafy terraces.
There is the poorer quarter, its homes a deep blue.
There is the market, where men are selling hats and swatting flies
And there is the public library, painted several shades of pale
green and beige.
Look! There is the square we just came from, with the
promenaders.
There are fewer of them, now that the heat of the day has
increased,
But the young boy and girl still lurk in the shadows of the
bandstand.
And there is the home of the little old lady —
She is still sitting in the patio, fanning herself.
How limited, but how complete withal, has been our experience
of Guadalajara!
We have seen young love, married love, and the love of an aged
mother for her son.
We have heard the music, tasted the drinks, and looked at colored
houses.

144

What more is there to do, except stay? And that we cannot do.
And as a last breeze freshens the top of the weathered old tower,
   I turn my gaze
Back to the instruction manual which has made me dream of
   Guadalajara.

A CLOSER LOOK

1. How does the poet use color (or the lack of it) to emphasize the contrast between the place where he's working and the place he's dreaming of? Point out several examples of his use of color.

2. In lines 6 and 7, the poet says, "I begin to dream . . . of dim Guadalajara." Why is Guadalajara "dim" in his mind?

3. In spite of the "dimness" of his mental picture of Guadalajara, the poet's description includes some details that are quite specific. Where might he have gotten these details? For example, where might he have gotten the idea that there is an "elaborate little bandstand" in the public square?

4. Does it matter that the poet's vision of Guadalajara is, strictly speaking, "not true"? Give reasons for your answer.

● In "Travel Song" the singer tells how he and other Eskimo hunters made the difficult journey by dog sled from the sea coast to their winter hunting grounds.

Anonymous

TRAVEL SONG

Leaving the white bear behind in his realm of sea-ice
we set off for our winter hunting grounds on the inland
    bays.
This is the route we took:
First we made our way across dangerous Dead-man's
    Gulch
and then crossed High-in-the-sky Mountain.
Circling Crooked Lake
we followed the course of the river over the flatlands
    beyond
where the sleds sank in deep snow up to the cross slats.
It was sweaty work, I tell you,
helping the dogs.

You think I even had a small fish
or a piece of musk-ox meat to chew on?
Don't make me laugh: I didn't have a shred on me.
The journey went on and on.
It was exhausting, pushing the sled along the lakes
around one island and over another,
mushing, mushing.
When we passed the island called Big Pot
we spit at it
just to do something different for a change.

Then after Stony Island
We crossed over Water Sound at the narrows,
touching on the two islands like crooked eyes
that we call, naturally, Cross-Eyed Islands,
and arrived at Seal Bay, where we camped,

and settled down to a winter season
of hunting at the breathing holes
for the delicious small blubber beasts — seals!

Such is our life,
the life of hunters,
migrating with the season.

(English translation by Edward Field)

A CLOSER LOOK

1. "Such is our life," says the singer in the last stanza. What kind of life is it? Do you think you would like this kind of life? Why or why not?

2. Some of the places mentioned in the song have names that suggest danger or difficulty. Find two examples.

3. Find two examples of humor in the song.

● The key to the meaning of this poem is hidden in the word "it."
The poet uses "it" to refer to a place, but he doesn't tell you where
the place is. However, he does seem to think that you will reach this
place someday, at which time, of course, you'll find out where it is.

Robert Creeley

OH NO

If you wander far enough
you will come to it
and when you get there
they will give you a place to sit

for yourself only, in a nice chair,
and all your friends will be there
with smiles on their faces
and they will likewise all have places

A CLOSER LOOK

*1. What kind of journey will you take to reach "it"? What
might this journey represent?*

*2. When you get there, what important thing will "they" do for
you? Who do you think "they" might be?*

3. How do you interpret the word "nice" in line 5?

*4. What is the difference in meaning between the following two
statements: (1) "Your friends will be there smiling." (2) "Your
friends will be there with smiles on their faces."*

*5. How do you think you will feel about being there? (The poet
predicts your reaction in two words. Can you find them?)*

● William Carlos Williams was a children's doctor whose busy practice left him little time for writing poetry. Perhaps because of this, he wrote many "snapshots" — short poems in which he captured a crisp image in only a few words.

William Carlos Williams

BETWEEN WALLS

the back wings
of the

hospital where
nothing

will grow lie
cinders

in which shine
the broken

pieces of a green
bottle

A CLOSER LOOK

1. The poet tells you that nothing will grow between the back wings of the hospital. On the basis of this hint, describe the area in back of the hospital. Try to include in your description a detail that explains why nothing will grow there.

2. The poet gives you a "snapshot" of the area between the wings. What two details does he mention?

3. Compare what is actually between the wings with what might be there (brown soil and green plants). What similarities do you see? What difference(s) do you see?

● When you look at a painting of a landscape, your eye is drawn from point to point by the artist's skillful composition, or arrangement, of elements in the scene. For example, you may first notice a bright cloud in the sky. From there your eye may follow the diagonal line of a hill down to the most important part of the picture: some cows lying under a tree. Something similar happens to the speaker in this poem, except that he is viewing an actual landscape, outdoors. As he looks and listens, his attention is drawn to a particular part of the scene that has special meaning for him. It seems almost as if Nature had composed the scene for his benefit.

Michael Heller

TWO SWANS IN A MEADOW BY THE SEA

High dunes falling away
To spongy ground, water lying
In brackish shallow pools
A few feet from the surf.

Broom and high grass hide
A dozen birds. They twitter.
We take it in as best we can,
The sea's sound, all
The marvelous growth.

No need to ask, to answer
How sky and hilly tufts,
Noise of cars on the road above

Are so composed to bring us,
Our eyes level with the sea,
To where two white forms
Rest their lovely necks
As though in self-caress,
Looking at each other.

A CLOSER LOOK

1. Is the speaker alone, or is there someone else with him? How do you know?

2. Swans, which mate for life, are often used as a symbol by artists and poets. What do they usually stand for?

3. What special meaning might the two swans have for the speaker?

● Well, it's November 3rd, and here's what's happening.

Richard Brautigan

NOVEMBER 3

I'm sitting in a café,
drinking a Coke.

A fly is sleeping
on a paper napkin.

I have to wake him up,
so I can wipe my glasses.

There's a pretty girl
I want to look at.

A CLOSER LOOK

1. Using clues in the title and the first four lines, describe the setting of the poem. What do you think the weather might be like? What kind of furniture and decoration does this café probably have? What's happening at the moment?

2. Instead of saying, "I have to brush it [the fly] off," the poet says, "I have to wake him up." Why is this humorous?

3. What is the very important sight that the poet wipes his glasses to see? Why does his eagerness to see it make us laugh?

4. The bare facts of the story might be stated like this: "While sitting in a café, the poet notices a pretty girl. He wipes his glasses so he can see her better." What does the poem have that this statement lacks?

• The "El" (elevated train) still runs in the part of New York City where this poem probably takes place. But candy stores like the one described are gone, along with the penny candy they sold.

Lawrence Ferlinghetti

THE PENNYCANDYSTORE BEYOND THE EL

The pennycandystore beyond the El
is where I first
                  fell in love
                              with unreality
Jellybeans glowed in the semi-gloom
of that September afternoon
A cat upon the counter moved among
                  the licorice sticks
          and tootsie rolls
          and Oh Boy Gum

Outside the leaves were falling as they died

A wind had blown away the sun

A girl ran in
Her hair was rainy
Her breasts were breathless in the little room

Outside the leaves were falling
        and they cried
                Too soon! Too soon!

A CLOSER LOOK

1. The boy in the poem (the speaker at an earlier age) loves the "unreality" of the penny-candy store. In what ways is the cozy world inside the store different from the "real" world outside? (The girl who runs in is a reminder of the real world.)

2. Why do the falling leaves cry, "Too soon, too soon"?

3. What part of the boy's life will too soon be over? What world will he have to face all too soon?

● "Further Arrivals" is based on the life of Susanna Moodie, a woman who immigrated into Canada from England in 1830. The poet learned about Susanna Moodie from reading the journals that she left behind. Originally, the poet had no intention of writing about Susanna. In fact, after reading the journals, she put them away and forgot about them. But eighteen months later she began to have strange dreams about Susanna. She then set down a series of poems in which Susanna speaks about the hardships and loneliness of the pioneers' life.

Margaret Atwood

FURTHER ARRIVALS

After we had crossed the long illness
that was the ocean, we sailed up-river

On the first island
the immigrants threw off their clothes
and danced like sandflies

We left behind one by one
the cities rotting with cholera,
one by one our civilized
distinctions
and entered a large darkness.

It was our own
ignorance we entered.

I have not come out yet

My brain gropes nervous
tentacles in the night, sends out
fears hairy as bears,
demands lamps; or waiting

for my shadowy husband, hears
malice in the trees' whispers.

I need wolf's eyes to see
the truth.

I refuse to look in a mirror.

Whether the wilderness is
real or not
depends on who lives there.

A CLOSER LOOK

1. What does Susanna mean when she describes the ocean as a "long illness"?

2. How did the immigrants express their joy at reaching land? Do you think they would have behaved like that if they had been back home in England? Why or why not?

3. In the third stanza, Susanna says that they left behind their city habits and civilized customs when they entered the wilderness. Give an example of a civilized custom that you would probably drop if you went to live in a wilderness. (To find an example, think of customs having to do with food, dress, housing, work, money, or entertainment.)

4. Susanna says that the wilderness was "a large darkness" to them because they knew nothing about it. And she admits that it still scares her. Find phrases in the poem that describe her fears.

5. Find lines in which Susanna suggests that a wilderness is not really a wilderness to one who understands it.

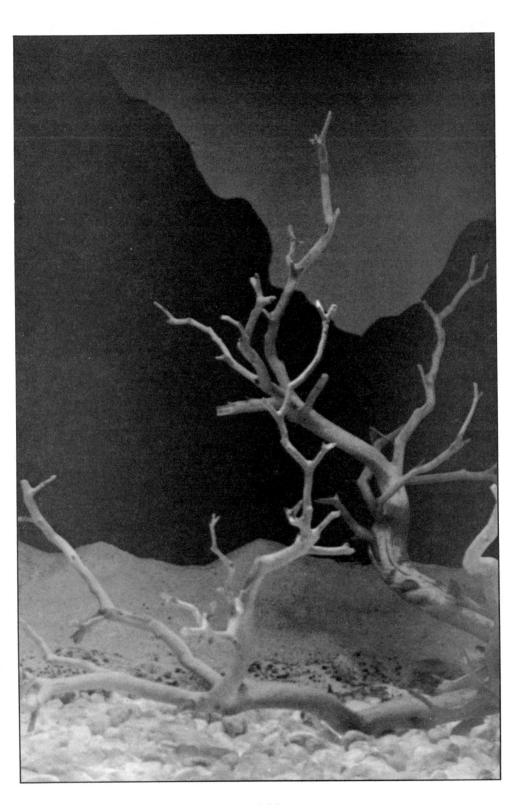

• For Native American tribes who lived by farming, the rain dance was an important tradition. Performers danced and chanted prayers, asking the clouds or the rain god to send rain to ensure a good crop.

Alonzo Lopez

DRY AND PARCHED

Dry and parched
The ground I stand on.
I sing a prayer.
I raise my arms.
I stamp my feet
And move in circles.
Dust rises
And the sun burns
But I keep dancing
And singing.
If I am pure and innocent,
I can call the rain
From the clouds.

A CLOSER LOOK

1. Why has the speaker chosen this time to perform the rain dance?

2. What details show that the dancer has reason to be discouraged?

3. What lines show that the dancer is determined to keep on trying?

4. What lines reveal the dancer's belief that the result depends on his character?

MEMORIES AND DREAMS

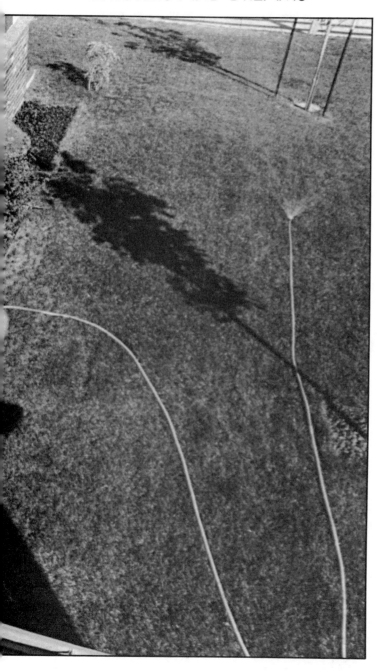

● Your hands are your obedient servants; you tell them what to do and they do it. This may be fine for you, but look at it from the hands' point of view. They might like to go places and do things by themselves. They might have a few things to say to you. Of course they can neither speak nor act on their own as long as you are awake. But you might be able to set them free — and learn something — by falling asleep.

Siv Cedering

HANDS

1

When I fall asleep
my hands leave me.

They pick up pens
and draw creatures
with five feathers
on each wing.

The creatures multiply.

They say: "We are large
like your father's
hands."

They say: "We have
your mother's
knuckles."

I speak to them:
"If you are hands,
why don't you
touch?"

And the wings beat
the air, clapping.
They fly

high above elbows
and wrists.
They open windows
and leave

rooms.
They perch in treetops
and under bushes biting

their nails. "Hands,"
I call them.
But it is fall
and all creatures
with wings
prepare to fly
South.

2

When I sleep
the shadows of my hands
come to me.

They are softer than feathers
and warm as creatures
who have been close
to the sun.

They say: "We are the giver,"
and tell of oranges
growing on trees.

They say: "We are the cup."

and I stir in my sleep.
Hands pull triggers

and cut
trees. But

the shadows of my hands
tuck their heads
under wings
waiting
for morning,
when I will wake
braiding

three strands of hair
into one.

A CLOSER LOOK

1. In the second stanza, the hands create creatures. Then they become those creatures. In what ways are the creatures like hands? In what ways are they like birds?

2. How do the creatures remind the dreamer that part of her comes from her father and part comes from her mother?

3. In the second part of the poem, the dreamer seems to enter a deeper level of sleep where she sees not the hands themselves but only their shadows. What clues tell you that these are the shadows of the birdlike creatures that she saw in part 1?

4. In the midst of her shadowy dream, the poet suddenly states a hard, cold fact about the waking world: "Hands pull triggers [while hunting, perhaps] and cut trees" [for farming, building, or firewood, perhaps]. Whose hands might the poet be referring to? (Give your opinion.)

5. Whose hands might the poet be referring to in the lines "We are the giver" and "We are the cup"? (Give your opinion.)

6. When she wakes up, the poet braids her hair. This act may simply be an example of the gentle domestic life she leads. Or the braiding of three strands into one may symbolize the combining of three elements in her life. If so, what might the three elements be? Here are two possibilities: (a) The three strands represent the poet's real hands, her dream hands, and the shadows of her dream hands. (b) The three strands represent her father's hands, her mother's hands, and her hands. Discuss your interpretation of the last three lines of the poem with your classmates.

● The ferry mentioned in this poem crosses New York Harbor between Manhattan and Staten Island. It was probably around 1920 that the poet took the rides she recalls in this "recuerdo," or memory.

Edna St. Vincent Millay

RECUERDO

We were very tired, we were very merry —
We had gone back and forth all night on the ferry.
It was bare and bright, and smelled like a stable —
But we looked into a fire, we leaned across a table,
We lay on a hill-top underneath the moon;
And the whistles kept blowing, and the dawn came soon.

We were very tired, we were very merry —
We had gone back and forth all night on the ferry;
And you ate an apple, and I ate a pear,
From a dozen of each we had bought somewhere;
And the sky went wan, and the wind came cold,
And the sun rose dripping, a bucketful of gold.

We were very tired, we were very merry,
We had gone back and forth all night on the ferry.
We hailed, "Good morrow, mother!" to a shawl-covered head,
And bought a morning paper, which neither of us read;
And she wept, "God bless you!" for the apples and pears,
And we gave her all our money but our subway fares.

A CLOSER LOOK

1. How many people took the rides described in this poem?

2. The poet and her companion(s) evidently went ashore one or more times between trips, in Staten Island (which was mostly rural in those days) or in Manhattan or both. Find lines that mention some of the things they did on shore.

3. About how old do you think the poet and her companion(s) were? What clues tell you that they were still in a happy-go-lucky mood in the morning as they headed toward the subway to go home?

- On the surface, this poem seems to be about a simple childhood experience. But on a deeper level, it is about the injustices that have been inflicted upon the native peoples of North, Central, and South America.

Ronald Rogers

KINDERGARTEN

In my kindergarten class
there were windows around the room
and in the morning we all took naps.
We brought our own rugs and crayons
because that was responsibility
and we learned to tell the colors apart.

Sometimes we read stories
about wrinkled old pirates with parrots
who talked about cities of gold.
And then we'd talk about cities of gold with streets of silver
and we'd laugh and laugh and laugh.

A CLOSER LOOK

1. In the first stanza the poet, a Native American, recalls the kindergarten that he and other Native American children attended. What two concepts or skills do the children in the poem learn? Are these concepts or skills part of the Native American culture, or are they part of the white man's culture?

2. In the second stanza, the pirates stand for all those who live by robbing others. Specifically, they stand for the European explorers who robbed the Central and South American Indians of their gold and silver. Even though the explorers did not find the "cities of gold" they were looking for, they found enough riches to make it worth their while to enslave the Indians. How do the children in the poem react when they hear that the white men believed in cities of gold? Do you think they are amused? scornful? bitter? Explain your answer.

● Have you ever wondered what strange law of memory makes you remember some things and forget others?

Alden Nowlan

HELEN'S SCAR

Helen, my cousin, says she still has the scar
from the time I pushed her out of the plum tree.

I don't even remember the plum tree.

"It must have been an accident," I say to her.
"It was no accident," she says. "You were mad at me."
She laughs. "It bled like the devil. I was scared to death."

How old were we then? Ten or eleven,
which means that she's seen that scar every day
for close to forty years
and will continue to see it
for the rest of her life.
It's not bad. But it's always there.

I did it;
and I don't even remember the plum tree.

A CLOSER LOOK

1. Find evidence in the poem that Helen wants the speaker to feel guilty about the scar he gave her.

2. What does Helen do to keep her words from sounding like a serious accusation?

3. Why doesn't the speaker remember the episode? (Give your opinion.)

4. Now that the speaker has been reminded of his misdeed, do you think he feels guilty? Give evidence from the poem to support your answer.

● Suppose you have painted a picture of a scene from your imagination. As you gaze at the picture, you feel almost as if you could step into it and be there, inside the scene. Well, go ahead: step right in. Now that you're inside the scene, look around. See if everything is exactly the way you pictured it. You say some things seem to be different? You say the scene seems to be changing even as you watch? Look over there, beyond the edge of the picture. What do you see? Whatever it is, that's where you're going. No, you can't go back; you have to go forward. Good luck!

Gregory Orr

THE ROOM

With crayons and pieces of paper, I entered the empty room.
I sat on the floor and drew pictures all day.
One day I held a picture against the bare wall:
It was a window. Climbing through,

I stood in a sloping field
at dusk. As I began walking, night settled.
Far ahead in the valley, I saw the lights
of a village, and always at my back I felt
the white room swallowing what was passed.

A CLOSER LOOK

1. *Which part of the poem is realistic? At what point does it become surrealistic (dreamlike)?*

2. *In line 4 the picture suddenly becomes a window. In what way is a picture like a window?*

3. *In real life, once a picture is finished, it remains the same forever. Within the picture, time stands still. What clues tell you that time does not stand still in the picture in this poem?*

4. *What is the white room swallowing? Toward what is the speaker walking?*

• Here's a dream: You're walking and walking, but no matter how long or how fast you walk, you can't seem to get where you want to go. Does this sound familiar? Then the feelings of the speaker in this poem will be familiar too.

David Ignatow

FROM A DREAM

I'm on a stair going down.
I must get to the landing
where I can order food
and relax with a newspaper.
I should retrace my steps to be sure,
but the stairs above disappear into clouds.
But down is where I want to go,
these stairs were built to lead somewhere
and I would find out.
As I keep walking,
ever more slowly,
I leave notes such as this on the steps.
There must be an end to them
and I will get to it,
just as did the builders.

if only I were sure now
that these stairs were built
by human hands.

A CLOSER LOOK

1. If this poem had no title, would you still know it was about a dream? Explain your answer.

2. Find a line in the poem that refers to the poem itself.

3. What kind of problem in real life might cause a person to have this kind of dream? (Give your opinion.)

● Light breaks when the sun comes up in the morning and drives away the darkness. "Light breaks" in our minds when a sudden insight brings understanding.

Lucille Clifton

BREAKLIGHT

light keeps on breaking.
i keep knowing
the language of other nations.
i keep hearing
tree talk
water words
and i keep knowing what they mean.
and light just keeps on breaking.
last night
the fears of my mother came
knocking and when i
opened the door
they tried to explain themselves
and i understood
everything they said.

A CLOSER LOOK

1. What do you think the poet means when she says that she knows the language of other nations? Here's a clue: She says "language," not "languages."

2. What do you think the poet means when she says she understands the sounds of trees and water?

3. Why is it important for the poet to understand her mother's fears? (Give your opinion.)

4. Did the poet's new understandings come to her slowly or suddenly? How do you know?

• If you have ever had a bad pain, you know that it seems to occupy your whole body. One way to keep from being overwhelmed is to mentally shrink the pain down so it is confined to the part of your body that actually has the injury. The poet calls this "singing the pain back into the wound."

Gregory Orr

SINGING THE PAIN BACK INTO THE WOUND

I crouch naked at the wound's edge
and call its name softly,
until it hovers over me and I am clothed
in its shadow. Then I throw ropes
over it, pulling it down into the wound
so that its body fits perfectly
like a fish-shaped cork.
Its wings beat frantically. I lash them together,
fold them carefully into a black
bundle on its back.

A CLOSER LOOK

1. At the beginning of the poem, where is the pain?

2. Why is it important to call the pain by its name?

3. Why does the poet want the pain to emerge from his body?

4. The poet gives the pain the wings of a bird. Do you think this is an appropriate image? Why or why not?

● When we are young, we dream many dreams of the future, which to us seems long and full of possibilities. When we are old, we may look back on those dreams as the most precious part of our lost youth.

Henry Wadsworth Longfellow

MY LOST YOUTH

Often I think of the beautiful town
   That is seated by the sea;
Often in thought go up and down
The pleasant streets of that dear old town,
   And my youth comes back to me.
      And the verse of a Lapland song
      Is haunting my memory still:
      "A boy's will is the wind's will,
And the thoughts of youth are long, long thoughts."

I can see the shadowy lines of its trees,
   And catch, in sudden gleams,
The sheen of the far-surrounding seas,
And islands that were the Hesperides
   Of all my boyish dreams.
      And the burden of that old song,
      It murmurs and whispers still:
      "A boy's will is the wind's will,
And the thoughts of youth are long, long thoughts."

I remember the black wharves and the slips,
   And the sea-tides tossing free;
And Spanish sailors with bearded lips,
And the beauty and mystery of the ships,
   And the magic of the sea.
      And the voice of that wayward song
      Is singing and saying still:
      "A boy's will is the wind's will,
And the thoughts of youth are long, long thoughts."

I remember the bulwarks by the shore,
    And the fort upon the hill;
The sunrise gun, with its hollow roar,
The drum-beat repeated o'er and o'er,
    And the bugle wild and shrill.
        And the music of that old song
        Throbs in my memory still:
        "A boy's will is the wind's will,
And the thoughts of youth are long, long thoughts."

I remember the sea-fight far away,
    How it thundered o'er the tide!
And the dead captains, as they lay
In their graves, o'erlooking the tranquil bay
    Where they in battle died.
        And the sound of that mournful song
        Goes through me with a thrill:
        "A boy's will is the wind's will,
And the thoughts of youth are long, long thoughts."

I can see the breezy dome of groves,
    The shadows of Deering's Woods;
And the friendships old and the early loves
Come back with a Sabbath sound, as of doves
    In quiet neighborhoods.
        And the verse of that sweet old song,
        It flutters and murmurs still:
        "A boy's will is the wind's will,
And the thoughts of youth are long, long thoughts."

I remember the gleams and glooms that dart
    Across the school-boy's brain;
The song and the silence in the heart,
That in part are prophecies, and in part
    Are longings wild and vain.
        And the voice of that fitful song
        Sings on, and is never still;
        "A boy's will is the wind's will,
And the thoughts of youth are long, long thoughts."

. . .

173

Strange to me now are the forms I meet
    When I visit the dear old town;
But the native air is pure and sweet,
And the trees that o'ershadow each well-known street,
    As they balance up and down,
        Are singing the beautiful song,
        Are sighing and whispering still:
        "A boy's will is the wind's will,
And the thoughts of youth are long, long thoughts."

And Deering's Woods are fresh and fair,
    And with joy that is almost pain
My heart goes back to wander there,
And among the dreams of the days that were,
    I find my lost youth again.
        And the strange and beautiful song,
        The groves are repeating it still:
        "A boy's will is the wind's will,
And the thoughts of youth are long, long thoughts."

A CLOSER LOOK

1. The poet's memory takes him back to the town where he lived as a boy. Where is the town located? Which parts of the town does he describe in greatest detail?

2. The poet says that islands in the seas were the Hesperides of his boyish dreams. He means that those islands were his idea of the most wonderful place to go. (In Greek mythology, the Hesperides was a garden where the golden apples of the gods were guarded by nymphs and a dragon.) Combining this with other information in the poem, what kind of life do you think the boy was dreaming about?

3. In what way is a boy's will like the wind's will? (To answer this question, decide what the wind's "will" — wish or desire — is.)

4. Explain the meaning of the last line of the refrain, "And the thoughts of youth are long, long thoughts." (In thinking about this question, consider the length of a youth's future and the remoteness of the places that the youth might be dreaming of.)

● Why does a child find it so deliciously exciting to do something that he knows he's not supposed to do? You may be able to answer from your own experience. If not, you'll find an answer in one line of this poem.

Theodore Roethke

CHILD ON TOP OF A GREENHOUSE

The wind billowing out the seat of my britches,
My feet crackling splinters of glass and dried putty,
The half-grown chrysanthemums staring up like accusers,
Up through the streaked glass, flashing with sunlight,
A few white clouds all rushing eastward,
A line of elms plunging and tossing like horses,
And everyone, everyone pointing up and shouting!

A CLOSER LOOK

1. *What happens in this poem? State the facts.*

2. *How does the poet use images of clouds and trees to express the child's sense of excitement and danger?*

3. *Why does the poet repeat the word "everyone" in the last line?*

4. *What satisfaction does the child get out of this adventure? Which line gives you the answer?*

● Try to remember a playground where you went as a child. What was your favorite activity in the playground? What toy or piece of equipment did you like best? The speaker in this poem gives highest praise to the sandbox.

Jake Hendrickson

THE SANDBOX

The sandbox

Was more
Than a sandbox
More
Than a slide
A jungle gym
And a green metal thing with holes
The little slide
Had steps
But the big slide made you climb the wooden wall
And when you went down the big slide
You shot into sand strayed out of the sandbox
There was a weird yellow jungle gym
It was round
And there were three pieces, all different sizes
If you got in the big one, you could blast off
And land on another planet
And when you landed you would
Run to the green metal thing
Hide under it and stick your arms out the holes
When the coast was clear you would run
To the sandbox and build a whole new kingdom
If you were lucky you could finish the castle
Before it was time to go home
If you were even luckier you could build
A bridge across the moat without it breaking
The next day
A new slide
A new journey
A new kingdom

The sandbox
Was more
Than a sandbox.

A CLOSER LOOK

1. Review the facts of the poem by telling how the child used the four kinds of playground equipment mentioned: the slides, the jungle gym, the "green metal thing," and the sandbox.

2. Why was the sandbox "more" to the child than a slide, a jungle gym, or a green metal thing with holes?

3. Why was the sandbox "more than a sandbox"?

● In this poem, one memory contains another. The poet remembers a day in his childhood when he sat on a porch listening to a woman tell about a day in her childhood.

Donald Justice

MEMORY OF A PORCH

Miami, 1942

What I remember
Is how the wind chime
Commenced to stir
As she spoke of her childhood,

As though the simple
Death of a pet cat,
Buried with flowers

Had brought to the porch
Some rumor of storms
Dying out over
A dark Atlantic.

At least I heard
The thing begin —
A thin, skeletal music —

And in the deep silence
Below all memory
The sighing of ferns
Half-asleep in their boxes.

A CLOSER LOOK

1. What event in her childhood did the woman tell about?

2. The subtitle of the poem, "Miami, 1942," tells you where and when the poem takes place. On what seacoast is Miami, Florida, located? What view do you think the people might have

been looking at as they sat on the porch? What world conflict was
going on in 1942? Where were some of the naval battles of that
war being fought?

3. Where did the breeze that stirred the wind chime come from?
The breeze came just as the woman was telling her story. Why did
the reminder of war brought by the breeze seem to fit in with the
woman's story?

● Have you ever "talked back" to an authority figure (in your head, that is)? That's what the speaker in this poem does, except that the voice that talks back isn't in his head. It's on his head.

Jacques Prevert

FREE QUARTERS

I slipped my cap into the cage
and went out with the bird on my head
So
you've given up saluting
asked the commanding officer
That's right

you don't have to salute anymore
answered the bird
Ah so
excuse me I thought everyone still saluted
said the commanding officer
You are fully excused everybody makes mistakes
said the bird.

(English translation by Michael Benedikt)

A CLOSER LOOK

1. *Describe the actions of the speaker in the poem. What does he do in the first two lines? What does he* not *do in line 4?*

2. *The speaker puts his military cap into the bird cage and takes the bird out. What might these two acts symbolize, or stand for?*

3. *The English title of this poem is a literal translation of the French title, "Quartier [quarters, meaning place of residence] Libre [free]." Another translator, Teo Savory, titled the poem "Off-Base." And there is a third possibility: "Off Duty." The title may come from the French idiomatic expression "avoir [to have] quartier libre," which means "to be off duty." In your opinion, which of these three titles best fits the poem?*

4. *Why do we enjoy seeing the speaker in this poem break the rules and get away with it?*

● As you probably know, a bagel is a tough, chewy roll made of plain yeast dough and shaped like a fat ring. You may have eaten many bagels, but have you ever chased one down the street?

David Ignatow

THE BAGEL

I stopped to pick up the bagel
rolling away in the wind,
annoyed with myself
for having dropped it
as it were a portent.
Faster and faster it rolled,
with me running after it
bent low, gritting my teeth,
and I found myself doubled over
and rolling down the street
head over heels, one complete somersault
after another like a bagel
and strangely happy with myself.

A CLOSER LOOK

1. Choose one of these three interpretations and explain why you think it makes sense. (If you can think of another interpretation, feel free to choose that one.) (a) The poem is realistic; everything in it could actually happen. (b) The poem is partly realistic and partly fantastic. (Tell where the dividing line is.) (c) The poem is all a fantasy or a dream.

2. No matter which interpretation you choose, you have to explain the portent in line 5. A portent is something that foretells or gives warning of a future event. What might the act of dropping the bagel foretell? (There is no certain answer. Just use your imagination.)

3. After the speaker gives up his two-legged chase and starts rolling along like a bagel, he feels "strangely happy" with himself. Why does he feel happy?

● Have you ever wondered why, every baseball season, millions of people get so wrapped up in something that's "just a game"? Here's one theory: It's not just a game. It's a drama in which players act out the game of life, with its competition and teamwork, its triumphs and defeats. While we watch this drama, we can pretend that the game of life and the game of baseball are alike. Of course, we know they aren't. In baseball, the rules are simple and understandable, and everybody obeys them. In baseball, the only way to succeed is through talent and hard work. In baseball, order and justice prevail.

Kenneth Patchen

THE ORIGIN OF BASEBALL

Someone had been walking in and out
Of the world without coming
To much decision about anything.
The sun seemed too hot most of the time.
There weren't enough birds around
And the hills had a silly look
When he got on top of one.
The girls in heaven, however, thought
Nothing of asking to see his watch
Like you would want someone to tell
A joke — "Time," they'd say, "what's
That mean — time?", laughing with the edges
Of their white mouths, like a flutter of paper
In a madhouse. And he'd stumble over
General Sherman or Elizabeth B.
Browning, muttering, "Can't you keep
Your big wings out of the aisle?" but down
Again, there'd be millions of people without
Enough to eat and men with guns just
Standing there shooting each other.

So he wanted to throw something
And he picked up a baseball.

A CLOSER LOOK

1. *The main character in the story seems to spend his time commuting between heaven and earth. What are some of the problems he observes on earth?*

2. *It seems that all kinds of people end up in the poet's version of heaven. Elizabeth Barrett Browning (a 19th-century English poet) represents a gentle life devoted to art. General William Tecumseh Sherman (a leader of Union armies in the Civil War) represents a life of violence. How do the people in heaven apparently spend their time? How do they feel about what is happening down on earth?*

3. *Why did the commuter want to throw something? What happened as a result of his throwing a baseball? Should we be glad that he happened to pick up a baseball instead of something else? Why or why not?*

● Have you ever gotten the urge to create a work of art, such as a poem, a story, a painting, or a piece of music? If you have, you'll be glad to hear that this poem tells you exactly how to go about it. But don't expect the usual kind of step-by-step instructions. The poem does give you steps to follow, but . . . well, you'll see.

Jacques Prevert

TO PAINT THE PORTRAIT OF A BIRD

First of all paint a cage
its door standing open
then paint
something appealing
something shining
something beautiful
something tasty
for the bird
then lean the canvas up against a tree
in a garden
in a forest
or in the woods
find another tree and hide yourself behind it
silently
without moving a muscle . . .
Sometimes the bird will come right away
but it could also take many long years
before it decides to
Don't become discouraged
but wait
wait if you have to year after year after year
the earliness or lateness of its arrival
has no relation
to the success of the work
When the bird appears
if he appears
maintain the most total silence

while you wait for the bird to enter the cage
and once he's in
softly shut the door with a quick stroke of your paintbrush
then
one by one blot out all the bars of the cage
taking care not to touch the bird's feathers
Then paint the tree's portrait
choosing the most beautiful of all its branches
for the bird
also paint the green foliage and the freshness of the breeze
the dust afloat in the sunlight
and the noises of the insects in the grass in the intense heat
   of summer
and then wait for the bird to sing
If the bird does not sing
it's a bad sign
a sign that the picture is bad
but if it does sing that's a good sign
that is to say a sign that you can sign
Then you reach out and gently pluck
one of the feathers of the bird
and you write your name over in one corner of the picture.

(English translation by Michael Benedikt)

A CLOSER LOOK

1. This poem is about how the human mind creates a work of art. The poet uses the process of painting a bird as a metaphor for what you do when you write a poem, for example, or paint a picture or compose music. The bird represents the idea or the effect that you're aiming at. Or, to put it another way, the bird represents the soul or the spirit of the work. Did you notice that the poet never tells you to paint the bird itself? Why does he leave out this step?

2. The bars of the cage represent the techniques or tricks you use when you write, paint, or compose. Why does the poet tell you to blot out, or erase, the bars?

3. The poet says that if the bird sings, it's a good sign. What does the bird's singing prove?

INDEX

187

189

ACKNOWLEDGMENTS *(continued from page 3)*

Harcourt Brace Jovanovich, Inc. for "Piazza di Spagna, Early Morning" from THINGS OF THIS WORLD copyright © 1956 and renewed 1984 by Richard Wilbur, reprinted by permission of Harcourt Brace Jovanovich, Inc. "Stars, Songs, Faces" from SMOKE AND STEEL by Carl Sandburg, copyright 1920 by Harcourt Brace Jovanovich, Inc. and renewed 1948 by Carl Sandburg, reprinted by permission of the publisher.

Harper & Row, Publishers, Inc. for "Mirror" from THE COLLECTED POEMS OF SYLVIA PLATH by Sylvia Plath. Edited by Ted Hughes. Copyright © 1960, 1965, 1971, 1981 by The Estate of Sylvia Plath. Reprinted by permission of Harper & Row, Publishers, Inc.

Michael Heller for "Two Swans in a Meadow by the Sea" from IN THE BUILDED PLACE. Reprinted by permission of the author.

Robert Hershon for "Openly Expressed Affection Between Members of the Family Unit." Reprinted from LITTLE RED WAGON PAINTED BLUE, Unicorn Press, copyright 1972 by Robert Hershon.

Henry Holt and Company for "Tree at My Window" by Robert Frost. Copyright 1928 by Holt, Rinehart and Winston and renewed 1956 by Robert Frost. Reprinted from THE POETRY OF ROBERT FROST edited by Edward Connery Lathem, by permission of Henry Holt and Company, Inc.

Houghton Mifflin, Inc. for "November 3" from THE PILL VERSUS THE SPRINGHILL MINE DISASTER by Richard Brautigan. Copyright © 1965 by Richard Brautigan. Reprinted by permission of Houghton Mifflin Company/Seymour Lawrence. "Young" from ALL MY PRETTY ONES by Anne Sexton. Copyright © 1962 by Anne Sexton. Reprinted by permission of Houghton Mifflin, Inc.

David Huddle for "Icicle." Reprinted by permission of the author.

Olwyn Hughes Literary Agency for "Mirror" by Sylvia Plath. From COLLECTED POEMS by Sylvia Plath, published by Faber & Faber, London, copyright Ted Hughes 1971, 1981, by permission of Olwyn Hughes.

Gloria Kagan for "The Room That's In Between" by Angela Lee; "My Sister Is Like a Balloon" by Christine Bader; "The Sight" by Jon Goldman; "The Sandbox" by Jake Hendrickson. Reprinted by permission of Gloria Kagan.

Little, Brown & Company for "First Lesson" from ABSENCES: NEW POEMS by James Tate. Copyright © 1970 by James Tate. First appeared in the *Emerson Review*. By permission of Little, Brown & Company.

Liveright Publishing Corporation for "Those Winter Sundays." Reprinted from ANGLE OF ASCENT, New and Selected Poems, by Robert Hayden, by permission of Liveright Publishing Corporation. Copyright © 1975, 1972, 1970, 1966 by Robert Hayden.

Macmillan Publishing Company for "For Anne Gregory" by W.B. Yeats. Reprinted with permission of Macmillan Publishing Company from THE POEMS OF W.B. YEATS: A NEW EDITION, edited by Richard J. Finneran. Copyright 1933 by Macmillan Publishing Company, renewed 1961 by Bertha Georgie Yeats. "Oh No" by Robert Creeley. Reprinted with permission of Charles Scribner's Sons, an imprint of Macmillan Publishing Company, from FOR LOVE: POEMS 1950-1960 by Robert Creeley. Copyright © 1962 Robert Creeley. "Something I've Not Done" by W.S. Merwin. Reprinted with permission of Atheneum Publishers, an imprint of Macmillan Publishing Company, from WRITINGS TO AN UNFINISHED ACCOMPANIMENT by W.S. Merwin. Copyright © 1970, 1973 by W.S. Merwin.

Suzi Mee for "My Father's Coat" and "My Father and My Sled," copyright © 1989 by Suzi Mee, and for "The Pineapple Event Poem," copyright © 1986 by Suzi Mee.

Samuel Menashe for "Reeds Rise From Water" from COLLECTED POEMS by Samuel Menashe. Published by The National Poetry Foundation, University of Maine, Orono, Maine 04469. Reprinted by permission of the author.

The Modern Poetry Association for "The Double-Play" by Robert Wallace. From VIEWS OF A FERRIS WHEEL by Robert Wallace. First appeared in POETRY © 1961 by The Modern Poetry Association. Reprinted by permission of the Editor of POETRY.

William Morrow & Company, Inc. for "A Poem for Carol" and "Knoxville, Tennessee" taken from BLACK FEELING, BLACK TALK, BLACK JUDGMENT, by Nikki Giovanni. Copyright © 1968, 1970 by Nikki Giovanni. "Chimneys" from SEARCH FOR THE OX by Louis Simpson. Copyright © 1971, 1973, 1974, 1975, 1976 by Louis Simpson. By permission of William Morrow and Co., Inc.

PHOTOGRAPHY CREDITS

All photographs are from the Scholastic/Kodak Photography Awards.

Pages 10-11: Christen Coia, Providence, RI. *Page 12:* Brigitta Shroyer, Middletown, OH. *Page 17:* Gayle Verbinski, Brockton, MA. *Page 23:* Mason Franklin, Dowagiac, MI. *Page 26:* Paul St. John, Martinsville, IN. *Page 30:* Peter Allen, Honeoye Falls, NY. *Page 33:* Joe Kinkade, Petaluma, CA.

Pages 34-35: Spence Smith, Topsfield, MA. *Page 37:* Jennifer Mariani, Burbank, CA. *Page 40:* Donna Hickernell, Myerstown, PA. *Page 43:* Dexter Laubach, Fort Benton, MT. *Page 45:* Lance Peeples, Melbourne, FL. *Page 47:* Franklin Juds, Largo, FL. *Page 49:* Susan M. Minard, Wayne, MI. *Page 52:* Jeff Gittleman, Pottsville, PA. Page 56: Karen Sternheimer, Beachwood, OH. *Page 59:* Sallie Sprague, Providence, RI.

Pages 62-63: Jay David Blumenfeld, St. Paul, MN. *Page 67:* Kelly King, Charlotte, NC. *Page 69:* Karin Boak, Lancaster, PA. *Page 74:* Matthew Ruzicka, Wappingers Falls, NY. *Page 77:* Bryan Horne, Burbank, CA. *Page 78:* Gary Campbell, Satellite Beach, FL. *Page 81:* Michelle Marcinko, Tucson, AZ. *Page 82:* Richard Greer, Tucson, AZ. *Page 84:* William Bonfiglio, Seattle, WA. *Page 87:* Joey Peterson, Bothell, WA. *Page 90:* Emily Cahan, Brookline, MA.

Pages 92-93: Gary Kellner, Strongsville, OH. *Page 98:* Bruce Rapoport, Mercersburg, PA. Page 102: Kimbrell Hill, Rochester, MI. *Page 107:* Todd Woodie, Downey, CA. *Page 109:* James Dieffernwierth, Burbank, CA. *Page 112:* Steven Heyden, Omaha, NE. *Page 117:* Stuart Culpepper, Norwalk, CT. *Page 119:* Michael Fellner, Baltimore, MD. *Page 122:* Heather Hurlston, Libertyville, IL.

Pages 128-129: Chris Lombardo, Reseda, CA. *Page 131:* Barbara Birdwell, Durham, NC. *Page 132:* Jerome LaLonde, Syracuse, NY. *Page 135:* Rick Hodgin, Cypress, CA.

Pages 138-139: Mark Nicholson, Stamford, CT. *Page 145:* Liz Valverde, Barrington, IL. *Page 147:* Paul R. McCormick, Fairbanks, AK. *Page 151:* Deborah Phillips, Stamford, CT. *Page 156:* Kimberly Reuswig, Syracuse, NY.

Pages 158-159: Mike Magner, Aurora, CO. *Page 166:* Mike Gulas, Raleigh, NC. *Page 168:* Ken Lam, Oakland, CA. *Page 177:* David Hensley, Tucson, AZ. *Page 179:* Kevin Mooney, Chicago, IL. *Page 183:* Vito Mazzara, Mt. Clemens, MI.